M000083349

Dear

Herbs ca... ... your

life !

Carol R. Peterson

Herbs You Can Master

A Primer for Herbal Enthusiasts

Carol R. Peterson

Mountain
Garden Publishing

The information in this book is true and complete to the best of our knowledge. All recommendations are made without guarantee on the part of the author or Mountain Garden Publishing, Inc. The author and publisher disclaim any liability incurred with the use of this information. This book is intended as a reference only, not as a medical herb manual or a guide to self-treatment. Be cautious on self-diagnosis or self-treatment of serious illness without competent professional assistance. The information presented here is not intended to substitute for any treatment that may have been prescribed by your physician.

Copyright © 1994 by Carol R. Peterson

All rights reserved. No part of this publication may be reproduced, stored in a retrieval system or transmitted, in any form or by any means, electronic, mechanical, photocopying, recording or otherwise, without prior written permission of the publisher.

Published by Mountain Garden Publishing, Inc.
P.O. Box 98
Snoqualmie, Washington 98065

Illustrator and cover design: Kate Rose
Copy Editor: Sharon Phillips
Technical Editor: Bob Lilly

Printed in the United States of America
First Printing, April 1994
Second Printing, December 1994
Third Printing, July 1995

Library of Congress
CIP 93-91797

Publisher's Cataloging in Publication Data:
Peterson, Carol
    Herbs You Can Master: A Primer for Herbal Enthusiasts

    Includes Index and Glossary

    ISBN 0-9639620-0-0

    1. Herbs 2. Herb gardening 3. Cookery (Herbs) 4. Herbs-Utilization
    5. Herbs-Therapeutic

Table of Contents

Note: for your convenience, each chapter in this book is made up of thirteen sections. Each of these sections is identified by its recognizable 'icon' or symbol. The sections are as follows:

1. Botanical Name
2. History
3. Type
4. Description
5. Planting and Care Requirements
6. Harvesting
7. Preservation
8. Propagation
9. Culinary Uses
10. Medicinal Uses
11. Other Uses
12. Recipes
13. Other Notes

Acknowledgements

My greatest thanks to Sharon Phillips who generously edited my draft copies and made them grammatically professional. To my readers Sue O'Donnell, Cathy & Fuzzy Fletcher, Kathy Maillet, Doris Toppen, Virginia Terrell, Mary Florek, Betty Carmichael, Sheryl Backus, and Robin Giese my appreciation for each one of you and your comments for clarification and encouragement. Much gratitude is given to the students in my many herb and cooking classes who have offered suggestions and valuable advice. Thanks to Mom, Pearl Jones, for her unwavering support throughout this project. A special heartfelt "thank you" to Julie Peterson for indispensable and voluntary public relations and media services. For the computer support and expertise Ryan Peterson and Dave Battey gave over many months, I am in your debt! To Charles for ongoing strength and all my errand-running, I give my heart.

Carol Peterson
Author

Introduction

This book has been many years in the making. Being an herb enthusiast since 1975, I have been asked hundreds of times to write down everything I know about the herbs I grow and use. Over this period of time, I have successfully grown about 100 different herbs in my Pacific Northwest garden. Of these, some are indeed a challenge, but each is special in its own way and supplies a need: its beauty, fragrance, taste, or all three — and more.

My general advice to people who have tasted my herbal cooking or admired my herbal decorative efforts is to begin with one or two herbs. Learn all you can about them, experiment with several varieties within the same genus, and then move on to another one or two. Learning to grow, harvest, preserve, cook, and decorate with herbs can be a lifelong hobby that is educational, relaxing, and most of all, fun.

Some words have a mystical sound: gold, chocolate, nectar, heaven, gem, check enclosed! Another word that qualifies for special admission is that dazzling word: herb. Indeed, "herb" may even outshine a metal or gems in its power to summon magical connotations. After all, gold and gems merely sparkle or beautify; chocolate and nectar only pique our taste buds; and heaven has still not come. But herbs not only sprinkle magic upon otherwise savorless food; they were, for centuries, the physician's primary source of help for the sick. Perhaps that is why herbs outnumbered gold two to one among the gifts bestowed by the Three Wise Men on the Christ Child.

For this book, I have selected ten of my favorite herbs that can easily be grown in our gardens and seem to be enjoyed by everyone. Some are well-known and others a little more unusual. You can say herbs (urbs — with a silent "H") as some do, or herbs (hurbs). Both pronunciations are correct. The British prefer to say herbs so as not to sound Cockney, but most people in America say urbs.

What exactly is the difference between herbs and spices? There are many answers to that question but my definition follows:

Herbs are plants, generally found in temperate zones. Their leaves and flowers contain distinctive essential oils which are used in food, medicine, cosmetic and decorative products.

Spices are the oil-containing seeds, barks, roots, or flowering parts of plants typically found in the tropics. They are used to flavor and help preserve food, as scents in perfumes, and sometimes in medicines.

The dictionary describes an herb as a plant that has a fleshy stem, as distinguished from the woody tissue of shrubs and trees. It generally dies back at the end of each growing season. Many of these "often aromatic" plants are used in medicine or as seasonings. Herbs can be of an annual, biennial, or perennial variety. I have included examples of each of these in this book.

I have read recently that the word "drug", which first appears in medieval literature, comes from a Teutonic word meaning "dried herb" or "dry barrel."

My ongoing fascination and study of herbs over many years has made me more appreciative of the uniqueness of nature. Man-made cars and buildings look alike, and prepared foods in little boxes and plastic wrap look alike. Plants, however, are beautiful, numerous, variable, changeable with the seasons, and stay in one place long enough to examine them — unlike birds and butterflies which fly away just when you get close enough to examine them. With plants, and especially herbs, you can bring in a leaf or flower to study and taste, or bring the whole plant into your house, condominium or apartment to live with you. They can become your friends and constant companions with their beauty, fragrance, and usefulness to your health, as well as make your everyday meals more exciting.

The ten herbs I'll discuss in this book are basil, chives, lavender, lemon balm, mint, oregano, parsley, rosemary, sweet cicely, and thyme.

I have chosen to present the information on each herb in the same format for easy reference and continuity. I hope it reads well and easily for you. I have additionally placed them in alphabetical order for quick reference.

It's my hope that this book will inspire every reader to try at least one of these herbs, whether you live in a house with a large yard, apartment with one sunny window sill, a condominium with a planter box on an outdoor balcony, or a small room with a hanging planter. It really is fun and easy — once you know how.

So, let's get started.

Basil

*Bet You Can't Grow
Just One*

Basil

S ome pronounce this herb with a long "A" sound, and others with the short "A" sound. Both are correct. The three most important things to remember about growing basil are *sun, heat, and patience!* With these you will be a great success. This is the most popular annual herb in America and is the subject of much adulation and festivities. **BASIL MANIA —** *bet you can't grow just one!*

 ## Botanical Name

Common Basil — *Ocimum basilicum* — is the most commonly purchased and available basil. It also produces twice the amount of leaves as most other varieties. This sweet basil has a taproot, square stems and can grow to 20 inches or more.

Japanese Lettuce Leaf Basil — *O. basilicum var. crispum* — has huge, light green, rather bubbly leaves that are easy to tear for pesto. This large leaf size is similar to a variety called 'Mammoth Basil,' which is easier to find in most nurseries. Both, however, aggravate the botrytis problem in Western Washington causing more black leaves and stems.

1

Aussie Sweetie Basil — *O. basilicum var. Aussie Sweetie* — was introduced in 1990. It has sweetly scented small leaves. These plants grow in columns about three feet high without any pinching.

African Blue Basil — *Ocimum var. African Blue* — is a highly ornamental hybrid basil. The beautiful light purple flowers grow on huge purple-green plants that can get as large as three feet high and as broad. This variety has a camphor aroma.

Holy or Sacred Basil — *O. sanctum tenuiflorum* — has an exotic spicy clove scent that refreshes any room or taste bud. It is sometimes sold as Spice Basil and goes well with cooked vegetables.

Spicy Globe Basil — *O. basilicum var. minimum* — is an import from Italy. It is a compact and dwarf variety that grows only to about 10 inches. Good for containers, a window box or as a lovely landscape border, this plant has small half-inch leaves and produces white flowers. It is highly ornamental with a wonderful flavor.

Lemon Basil — *O. basilicum basilicum var. citriodorum* — needs continual watering during drought conditions and likes plenty of organic matter. Its pointed leaves are light green with a strong lemon fragrance. It will grow about a foot tall and produce an abundance of white flowers. This variety is especially good in salads.

Cinnamon Basil — *O. basilicum var. Cinnamon* — is a compact annual with dark green leaves, purple bracts and flowers, and purple-green stems that can be used both for Cinnamon Basil oil and vinegar for a lovely vinaigrette. This basil is more drought resistant than Lemon Basil and grows somewhat larger. It has a rich, Sweet Basil scent topped with a spicy cinnamon perfume. See a recipe below using this flavor. It is also especially favored for potpourri.

Licorice Basil — *O. basilicum cv.* — makes a refreshing tea and is useful in many culinary dishes.

Dark Opal Basil — *O. basilicum var. purpurascens* — is especially good in flavored vinegars and jellies because it gives a lovely soft violet color. This highly aromatic herb has medium-large dark leaves that are somewhat fringed and creates a wonderful contrast to lighter-colored plants in a mixed planting.

Purple Ruffles — *O. basilicum 'Purple Ruffles'* — is a cross of Dark Opal Basil with a new strain of lettuce leaf basil. Its large dark purple leaves and pale pink flower spikes have a strong aromatic scent and is also very decorative. This plant can grow 18-20 inches tall.

Camphor Basil — *O. x kilmandscharicum* — can be used as a culinary herb, but the fuzzy leaves smell like mothballs and are better used as an insect repellent in your closets.

The basil family **Labiatae** also contains the mint group.

 # History

Basil is a native plant to India, Africa, Iran and Asia and is cultivated extensively in France, Egypt, Hungary, Indonesia, Greece, and Italy. Wild basil, *Clinopodium vulgare,* a plant related to basil, is native to Europe and widely naturalized in North America, having dense clusters of small pink or purplish flowers.

The word "basilikom" in Greek means "royal" or "basileus" meaning "King;" an apt name for this much-loved herb. It has also previously been known as St. Josephwort, but I think basil has a much nicer tenor!

The Greeks and Romans of ancient times considered basil to be a symbol of hostility or insanity. Sowing basil in French means "ranting." The Greeks and Romans believed that to sow basil successfully you had to shout and swear while planting the seeds — hence the insanity. If you want to see if this is a myth or not, try sowing basil seeds, curse them soundly and tell them to stay in the ground, and see if it helps or not.

In mythical history, it was thought to be the herb that was used by Salome to hide the head of John the Baptist. Basil in a shredded form was scattered over the grave of Mohammed, and the ancient Egyptians included the root in the sarcophagus for royal entombments.

Stories of love have also been told about this herb. In Northern Europe, lovers exchanged basil sprigs as signs of faithfulness. In India, it has long been thought to be a sacred herb, hence their native species, *Ocimum sanctum,* "holy basil". Haitian shopkeepers sprinkle basil water around their stores to ward off evil spirits and to bring them prosperity.

TYPE: Annual *(tender)*

An annual is a plant that can be sown from seed and will mature in a single growing season to flower and then again to form seed. It completes its full life cycle in one season. An annual seed should not be sown until all danger of frost is past.

Basils grown in the Southwest are considered tender perennial plants if protected from temperatures below 55° F. In the Pacific Northwest, however, it is very unlikely that a basil plant will survive outside in winter, even a mild one. A tender annual is one which will not survive even one season in temperatures below 50° F.

Description

Basil is an annual plant with leafy stems that give it a bushy appearance. It's fast growing and prolific under the right conditions. The leaves are very fragrant and lay opposite each other on the stem, oval with toothed or smooth edges, depending on the variety. These leaves are sometimes two to three inches long and can be yellow-green to dark green depending on the variety and the soil fertility. Basil produces tiny, dark brown seeds and a variety of flower colors. There are many varieties of basil available at nurseries today, each with its own botanical name, which sometimes identifies its flavor. There are generally three kinds of basil plants, Sweet, Bush, and other.

Sweet Basil

Sweet basil has largish, shiny dark green leaves and can grow one to two feet high in an ideal, warm environment.

One of the popular hybrid forms of Sweet Basil is *Opal Basil* which has dark purple leaves and pink to lavender flowers. It usually reaches about one foot in height and has large leaves two and one half inches wide by one and one half inches long. It gives good color contrast in the garden and is very useful in cooking. Plant Opal Basil with marigolds to make a striking arrangement in the summer garden. A recipe for the rich, ruby color this basil gives to vinegar follows at the end of this chapter. The sweetly perfumed leaves make a colorful addition to salads and look quite appealing sprinkled over slices of ripe red (or yellow!) tomatoes. A delicious and very colorful pesto can also be made with Opal Basil, but it is very pungent.

Japanese Lettuce Leaf Basil is one of the oldest classic basil strains, aptly named for its voluminous green leaves. It offers a wonderful fragrance from big leaves that sometimes grow to four inches in width. Harvest the mildly spicy, sweetly flavored leaves all summer by pruning back to a second set of leaves whenever you harvest. These leaves can be shred right into a mixed salad bowl, or can be used instead of lettuce on all kinds of sandwiches. These giant leaves make good 'wrappers' to stuff with cheese mixtures and serve as tasty and simple appetizers.

Bush Basil

Bush basil grows only about six to eight inches high but is bushy and quite compact — not sprawling. The leaves are usually pale green with white flowers.

French Fine Leaf (or Spicy Globe), Licorice and Piccolo Basils are additional bush basil varieties that are desirable for their fragrances as well as multiple culinary uses.

Other Basils

Other basil includes those similar to Bush but that grow taller than this diminutive variety. Several of these varieties include the following:

Holy Basil is a very popular variety of Bush Basil used in cooking. The long pointed leaves of the Holy Basil plant are easy to pick and preserve.

Cinnamon Basil is a marvelous strain of pretty pink-flowering basil with an exotic perfume. Its spicy scent fills the air when you brush against it in the garden. The vigorous plants have dainty flower spikes and shiny green leaves, and both the flowers and leaves have an intense cinnamon fragrance combined with basil's sweet essence. These leaves make a delightful and delicate jelly, chutney, a fine herbal tea, and a sweet surprise in fruit salads. This classic plant can also be used in curries, sweet-and-sour dishes, rib and chicken marinades, or wherever you fancy its particular flavor.

Lemon Basil has fine leaves, is low-growing and has a concentrated clear lemon fragrance mingled with the familiar basil-clove perfume. It can be used liberally in seasoning steamed or sauteed vegetables, rice dishes, fish, poultry or added to salad dressings. These diminutive plants grow to one foot tall with small pointed leaves. Try its crushed leaves steeped with mint over ice on a hot summer day. These plants also spurn Japanese-beetle pests.

A newer variety, *Anise Basil,* is now available in some seed catalogues and is very similar to the basil that is used most frequently in Thai cooking. This is the one basil that can be used in desserts because of its sweetness. You might like to try it with poached pears, baked apples or in melon salads. This basil has fringed green leaves and rosy-colored flower stalks.

Basil produces a clove-like flavor with subtle mint undertones that is very distinctive and pleasant. Once you have tasted a basil culinary recipe, you won't forget its unique aroma and flavor.

Friends from Riverview Farm in Fall City, Washington have some definite opinions about basil, their favorite crop. Emil

Giese tells me that they harvested 11,262 pounds of basil in 1992. His Italian customers find their way to the fields by following their noses to the 'pesto patch.' Robin Giese had to baby-sit the basil crop one cool evening as Emil was sure that it wasn't growing. She dutifully went out with a flashlight to check on their babies and then reassured Emil that his crop was doing just fine! They grow only broad-leaf Sweet Basil for their customers and Emil states that growing Purple Ruffles Basil is like growing flowering kale — nice to look at, but not very productive for culinary uses.

 ## Planting & Care Requirements

Basil, like most herbs, needs a sunny location (at least five to six hours of direct sunlight a day). The light develops essential oils in the leaves. The essential oils impart a strong fragrance and taste from the herb and can actually be felt on the leaf surfaces. Some basil, like Opal Basil, has quite dark leaves while others like Lemon or Cinnamon variety have a lighter color. Mottled, variegated or curled varieties are also available but these are weaker and prone to fungus disease and root rot. They are still well worth growing for their beauty and variety. Full daily sun is important for all leaf colors and basil, in general, detests cool weather and cold soil. Remember, full sun!

Well-drained soil is essential for basil to grow productively and a pH of 6.0 is ideal. Humus and rich nutrients are essential to keep your basil growing well. Some peat moss and lime can be added to help the pH balance. Basil does not tolerate "wet feet" as mints do and can actually be planted in a soilless potting medium (check with your garden center) as this encourages a good root system.

If you choose to grow basil from seed and buy a seed packet but can't plant immediately, it's best to place the packet in a jar with a tight-fitting lid and put in the refrigerator as the seeds will stay fresh this way. If you start your seeds indoors, follow the package directions. Don't start too early, however, as basil germinates and begins growing quickly and the plants may be ready to transplant outdoors before the weather and soil have warmed up sufficiently. When the first true set of leaves appear, the seedlings can be transplanted either to individual larger pots indoors or into your outdoor garden if the conditions are right. Basil seeds should be started indoors several weeks before the last frost date if you plan to transplant outdoors for summer. Our last frost date is around the first week of May in King County, Washington. Seeds can also be planted directly into the garden, but if the ground is too cold, they may rot with a too early sowing. These time frames will give your plants a few weeks start on the growing season.

If you choose not to start from seeds, starter plants can be purchased in the spring and then put outdoors during the days *only when the temperatures are regularly above 60-65° F.* and placed permanently in your garden when the temperatures are steadily at 50° F. or more at night. For good drainage, you may add perlite, sand or other organic matter to your prepared soil. *Basil cannot tolerate temperatures below 50° F.* and, therefore, cannot be planted outside in the spring in our area until the nighttime temperatures are at least at that level. This usually means into June. The first sign of a cool day or night will turn the leaves dark and they will begin to wilt. Remember heat!

When first planting or transplanting your basil, it's a good idea to pinch the stems back to a full set of leaves when plants are six inches tall to encourage branching. (Of course, you are going to add those leaves to your salad that night. I wouldn't think of wasting even one!) This pinching can also be done at other times during harvest to stimulate an abundant supply as well as to keep the plants bushy and healthy. Remember, patience!

If your basil is planted in a container, be sure to check the water frequently on very warm days. They dry out faster in a container than they do when planted in the ground. If inner leaves drop green from the plant, it indicates too much water in the soil. Yellowing of the leaves can be caused by too little water or sometimes lack of nutrients. If a drought is expected, it is best to mulch around the basil plants — after the soil warms up. This will prevent drying the roots out while keeping the plants warm.

Basil makes a good plant for a front border and can be planted in vegetable or flower gardens. Planting near tomatoes makes it easy to pick both at once for an outstanding taste treat (even while you're still in the garden!). A combination of Sweet Basil and Opal Basil do nicely in window boxes.

Basil, like most herbs, does not need to be fertilized if the planting soil is rich in nutrients. You may, however, want to use a small amount of liquid fish fertilizer emulsion (or a 20-20-20 mix diluted) to get the plants started and after a heavy harvest to increase the production. Too much fertilizer, however, will affect the amount of essential oils your plant produces — too much fertilizer, too little oil. Remember, the oil is the reason you grow basil in the first place. I do use homemade compost in my herb beds, but basil does not like a very rich soil. After all, most of them come from the dry areas around the Mediterranean Sea in the Middle East.

A wonderful thing about basil (and many other herbs) is that the bugs (insects to entomologists) don't particularly bother them. Aphids can sometimes be a problem but using a good quality insecticidal soap will eliminate them for days at a time. Japanese beetles can attack basil but can be shaken off into a bucket of warm water with salt and detergent added. Very young basil should be protected from snails and slugs. Slug damage can be seen easily by the ragged holes or edges on the leaves. These 'slug thugs' can be controlled by picking them off at night if you want to spend some quality time with your children after dark with a flashlight. Another way to eliminate these despicable destructos is to put rubbing alcohol and liquid detergent or cooking oil in a pump spray or a large squirt gun and — ready, aim, fire! If you, and your children, are good shots, you may eliminate most of them in one night. Once the aromatic basil leaves are off the ground the slugs usually leave them alone. Actually, I have so many other things that the slugs like, they don't chew on my basil much, thank goodness. Sometimes I even plant extra things they like better (lettuce and green beans) nearby to give them something to munch on while my basil and other herbs grow heartily along.

Caterpillars sometimes cause damage, and plants can be treated with bacillus thuringiensis (b.t. for short), but remember, this is an insecticide, and shouldn't be used if you plan to harvest the leaves within a few days. Always follow the instructions on the label when using chemical products for insect or disease control.

Aside from slugs and worms, a fungus (both airborne and soil borne types) can be a problem with damp cool conditions. Plant late to prevent this from occurring.

 **Harvesting**

Basil should be picked in the morning after the dew is off the leaves. This gives the plant a chance to give off its essential oils from the stems into the leaves as the day starts to warm. When picking just a few leaves to use at a time, it is best to pinch back several stems leaving two or three sets of leaves on each stem. Each of these remaining stems will then branch into two or more new stems and continue to create a bushy, healthy plant. Never pick just a leaf or two from the plant as this will not allow it to branch.

Pick the stems and leaves before the plants flower. Once flowering has occurred, much of the essential oils will go into the flower production. Another reason to keep the flowers pinched off is to prevent cross-pollination of your basil varieties. Of course, you can also use the flowers in a variety of ways I will discuss later. Picking the flowers from the stems will not prevent the flowers from forming again. The plant must be cut deeply to encourage the vegetative growth. Basil *likes* to be picked regularly to keep it bushy and healthy. After a large harvest, twice as many branches will shoot up and a second full harvest can be made in three to four weeks. Fertilize after each major harvest for your production to continue.

Before frost, the plant can be a.) completely cut to ground level to preserve all the remaining harvest; b.) left to set seeds for the next season, if your climate is mild; or c.) brought into the house to be kept throughout the winter on a sunny window sill. One caution about indoor basil — it does have a tendency to attract spider mites easily. To rid them permanently, an insecticide must be used which is not safe on an edible plant. A spray with an insecticidal soap, again, can be effective if you catch the little critters early. You also might want to try using Tanglefoot (a sticky substance) on a neon-colored card to attract them. I have found this method quite successful when I want to bring the plants indoors. Because my individual basil plants give me so much harvest in the four months they grow, I generally don't try to keep them in the house much longer when the summer weather begins to cool at night. Some of my friends, however, have had great success with indoor basil gardens. Remember heat, sun and patience!

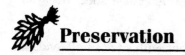 **Preservation**

Freezing is the best way of preserving basil, but it *may* be dried as well. I have found that preserving by drying (or dehydrating) does not produce the long-term flavor that is achieved by freezing. However, I will share with you both techniques as well as many different ways to use this herb.

For either process of preserving, pick the basil stems, remove the leaves and rinse them gently in cool water, then pat dry on paper toweling or a terry towel. If moisture remains on the leaves — whether dried or frozen — they will turn quite dark. Although this doesn't really affect the taste, it isn't as pretty or appetizing as the green color.

To dehydrate this herb, and most others, it is much better to use a commercial dehydrator, like the *Living Foods Dehydrator*, a wonderfully effective wooden dehydrator made in Fall City, Washington. (See the Glossary.) Either an oven or microwave can be used, however, but with less than superior results. The dehydrator temperature should be between 100° and 110° F. After patting the leaves dry, place on dehydrator racks, separating the leaves so that they do not overlap. Some dehydrator racks don't have to be rotated, but you should watch to see that the leaves don't get too crumbly. This might take only a few hours or a day or two depending upon the humidity and temperature, how full your dryer is, and other factors. After drying, carefully place leaves in a jar without crumbling them. Cover tightly and keep in a cool, dry place until use. You can check the jars a day or two after storage to be sure no condensation has appeared, which is a sure sign they weren't dry enough.

Another tip for successful storage, if you use a jar for the dried basil, use only the size needed to hold the supply as extra air in the jar will age the basil at a faster rate.

Because the temperature in most kitchen ovens does not go below 150° F., the leaves usually dry too rapidly, dissipating the oil and reducing the flavor further. If using an oven, be sure to keep the door ajar slightly so that accumulated moisture can escape. Again, the leaves need to be placed on a rack that will allow air under and over the leaves. A cookie sheet does not work well.

Microwave ovens can also be used but with such small loads in the oven the magnetron tube may be damaged. Over time the tube may be ruined if it is not shielded from microwaves that have nowhere to go when the moisture is evaporated and the moist air is vented off the oven. You can add a small amount of water in a microwave proof container in the oven to prevent any long-term damage. Because the drying process in the microwave needs to be monitored closely, herbs dried in this way have a tendency to cook before they are dried. This is particularly true of basil.

Harvested basil plants may be hung and air dried as well as frozen and oven dried, if kept away from humidity and too much light. Detailed instructions on drying of herbs was usually omitted from early books because these techniques were common knowledge, but today we need a refresher course in this type of preservation.

To freeze the basil, again pick the stems in the morning before flower spikes are produced. If you wait until after the flowers appear, you will lose much of the aroma and taste. Rinse the leaves if they are dusty (I tend to pick mine after a rain — which is pretty frequent in the Seattle area). Dry them well and layer them in a tight-lidded freezer container. You may also want to try placing the towel-dried fresh leaves on a cookie sheet. Place in the freezer section of your refrigerator to freeze lightly and then bag them or layer in a freezer container. When you use these leaves you can peel off the amount you need and freeze the rest. If several extra leaves thaw in the process, don't refreeze them as they will lose much of their flavor and nutrients. Instead, use them right away. Another way to freeze fresh basil leaves is to stack several in each block of an ice cube tray and cover with water and freeze. These frozen cubes can then be removed from the tray and placed in plastic bags for later use. This of course, will produce a darker leaf, but it is still very edible and tasty.

Frozen basil can be kept for six months or more. I always run out by then so I don't know if it might keep for a year. Dried basil will keep even longer if it is kept completely moisture free.

Three further ways that basil can be preserved are in olive oil, salt or vinegar. I have tried all of these when I have an abundant crop, resulting in more alternatives for later use. For making a wonderful basil oil, layer the clean, dry leaves with olive oil and a little mashed garlic in a glass jar with a wide top, pressing down well between the layers. Cover with a lid and store in the refrigerator. Out of refrigeration, storage could cause botulism if conditions are right, therefore, I always recommend storing at 40° F. or below. Botulism toxin occurs when foods are kept at inappropriate temperatures (between 40° and 140° F.) in an airless environment. Foods that become contaminated with botulism can cause severe neurological damage and sometimes death.

Basil leaves can also be mixed with equal amounts of table or sea salt in a blender to make basil salt. After combining the ingredients well, I dry the mixture on waxed paper for a day or two before storing. This is a real treat sprinkled on vegetables in the middle of winter, or used on fresh corn-on-the-cob. I tried this for the first time two seasons ago when my basil harvest was bountiful. I called the experts at The Herbfarm in Fall City and they gave me this simple storage idea! Small jars of this basil salt also make wonderful hostess gifts.

For preparation of basil vinegars, see the Recipe Section. Opal Basil vinegar is a particular favorite but other varieties, licorice, cinnamon, or lemon, are equally good.

Propagation

For propagation of this herb, I have found it best to grow basil from seed. I usually plant a whole package of seeds, such as Sweet Basil, all at once which gives me bushels of basil. **BASIL MANIA** — *I know that I can't grow just one!*

The disadvantage of this method is that you get many basil plants but all of the same variety. Of course, you can always give small pots with several transplanted basils in them to friends. Refer to the previous section on **Planting and Care Requirements** for more information.

Cuttings of plants can also be taken, however, it tends to lessen the vigor of the "mother" plant. For cuttings, take a six-inch stem of the basil plant and remove any leaves from the bottom two inches. Place in a glass of water until roots form. This cutting can then be planted in potting soil with a small amount of fertilizer applied.

 **Culinary Uses**

Basil is best known in our area for its many uses in cooking. It can be used in recipe preparation from soups to desserts. Basil is the Grandaddy or Grandma of the herb family as far as many people are concerned and is the main reason they plant an herb garden. In fact I have a friend who says he has an 'herb garden,' but it contains just three basil plants. That's all he needs.

Basil is considered a medium-flavored herb that can be used in the quantity of one to two teaspoons of fresh herb per six servings. Basil's flavor blends well with many other herbs, especially Lemon Thyme, parsley, chives, and garlic.

Basil is as popular in the cuisines of Southeast Asia, especially Thai and Vietnamese, as in those of Italy, and, of course, here in America.

There are *so* many culinary uses — where to begin? Of course! PESTO, that rich, oily, green paste that celebrates summer breezes and basil. Pesto originated in Genoa, Italy to flavor pasta. The French use it in soup and call it *pistou*. My best recipe for pesto follows and it's important to use fresh ingredients to take advantage of the lovely basil color and flavor. You can certainly substitute for the pine nuts, or omit them altogether if you choose, as they are expensive. I wish I knew an outlet where I could buy them by the pound because they do keep very well in the refrigerator or freezer. I make several other herb varieties of pesto as well as this one with basil, so you might want to experiment a little in your kitchen, too.

When using dried basil, crush the leaves lightly just as you add them to the recipe. This will release the oils at the very last minute. When cooking with dried or frozen basil, do not add to the recipe until the last 10-15 minutes. Too much cooking, or cooking over too high a heat will evaporate the fragrance and the delicate taste. The dried basil, although inferior to the fresh or frozen, can be used in the same way as fresh basil, with the exceptions of pesto sauce and vinegar. I have not had a great deal of success making these with dried basil. I have given you a couple of other ways to use basil for cooking at the end of this chapter.

Basil leaves are wonderful in salads in small quantities, especially with a fresh *Mesculn* salad of miniature greens. Most basil varieties are excellent with fish, cheese, vegetables and especially *tomatoes*. The Japanese variety, Lettuce Leaf Basil, resembles curly-leafed lettuce. With its milder flavor, it can be used as wrappers for fillings of boiled shrimp, shredded chicken or pork, or chopped vegetables and then dunked into lively sauces. For a very nutritious and satisfying side dish, these large leaves can also be wrapped around *Tabbouleh*, a Middle Eastern rice salad.

I keep one jar of mixed Italian herbs in my cupboard especially for spaghetti, pizza and everything Italian. This is the one exception to the dried basil rule. A mix of several dried herbs is my number one seasoning. I even sent it regularly to our son, Ryan, when he was in college to spice up his dormitory-type pizzas.

Besides pesto, my favorite use of fresh basil in the kitchen is the recipe below for broiled tomatoes. Please try it, I know you'll love it, too.

As an herbal tea, Cinnamon Basil is reminiscent of Indian spice tea. This unusual variety can also be combined with hibiscus flowers, Lemon Balm and/or blackberry leaves for a stimulating tea combination.

 # Medicinal Uses

Basil has never been considered a 'major healing herb,' but has been used to treat a variety of conditions. It is used as a laxative, for travel sickness, headaches and tension, as well as for skin infections such as acne. Other ailments which seem to subside with basil are indigestion, muscle spasms, vertigo and colic. Usually the herb is used in an infusion for these purposes. (See Glossary.)I recently had a mildly severe case of nausea and vomiting and tried eating just three fresh basil leaves. After being miserable for three to four hours, the nausea and vomiting subsided within two minutes after ingesting the basil leaves. I wondered why I waited so long to think of it!

An infusion is made like tea but used more medicinally rather than as a beverage. A traditional infusion recipe calls for one half to one ounce of dried basil (or other herb) steeped in a pint of boiled water for 10-12 minutes. Infusions do not keep well, therefore they should be made as needed. Another measure might be one half teaspoon of herb per cup of boiled water steeped for the same amount of time. You can use fresh herbs instead of dry as well by doubling or tripling the amount. One cup of tea infusion can be drunk up to three times a day for good relief of symptoms.

? Other Uses

Basil is best used in cooking but can be used in some cosmetic and decorative ways as well. With so many varieties available, you can create unending combinations.

Add Lemon, Licorice, or Cinnamon Basil to a *potpourri* or sleep pillow. Arrange some of the stems with flower spikes (if you let them go that long) in a vase with fresh flowers, especially the Opal or Purple Ruffles varieties. Basil can also be used along with marjoram, lovage and thyme in a spicy *'eau de toilette'* (herbs soaked in vodka!). Another use is in a muslim bag along with other herbs for a soothing bath.

Basil is wonderful in a blend with rosemary as a hair rinse for brunettes. It leaves a lovely fragrance as well as a shine to the hair. For a hair rinse, use an infusion that has cooled enough, for a final rinse.

 Recipes

And now to the most important part — cooking (or not cooking) and eating this wonderfully delicate herb. So many recipes abound using basil, it was very difficult to choose just a few for this book. Please try each one of the following during the summer basil season.

My Best Pesto Recipe

Combine one cup of packed, **fresh basil leaves,** three tablespoons of **pine nuts** (or **walnuts,** chopped), three tablespoons of grated **Parmesan cheese,** and two to three cloves of **garlic.** Puree in food processor (or by hand with a mortar and pestle). Add a good olive oil by drizzling until a smooth paste forms.

Making and spreading this wonderful paste on almost everything edible can become addicting! By the way, the word "pesto" means "to pound." A mortar and pestle were originally used to make this remarkable and tasty condiment, but busy, modern cooks usually use the food processor method, especially if you make as much of this as I do. Use *pesto* on pasta, vegetables, pizza, to stuff under the skin of roasted turkey or on bread or crackers. I have also used it as an appetizer by hollowing out tiny tomatoes and stuffing with pesto. My guests love it!

Lemon Basil and almonds make a wonderful pesto combination as does Purple Ruffles with some chopped sun-dried tomatoes. The possibilities are endless when you have a good choice of basil varieties.

Italian Herb Mix

Combine two tablespoons **dried basil,** one tablespoon each of **dried oregano, marjoram, thyme,** and **crushed rosemary.** Use as a salad seasoning, or in a salad dressing with oil and vinegar, with oil as a marinade for fish or chicken, or on steamed vegetables. And, of course, as I said earlier — on all Italian type dishes — pizza, spaghetti, lasagna, etc.

Keep this mixture in a glass jar with a stopper, but not near the stove, please, as extra heat will dissipate the flavor.

Broiled Tomatoes

Use fresh, large **tomatoes,** such as Beefsteak or Early Girl. Be sure they are firm. One large tomato will serve two. Slice tomato in half horizontally, after removing the core. **Salt and pepper** the cut sides lightly. We like ground sea salt and fresh ground multi-colored pepper. Sprinkle with chopped **fresh basil leaves** (or pesto), **grated Parmesan cheese,** and **bread crumbs.** Drizzle tops of tomatoes with **olive oil** and broil lightly, about five to ten minutes.

This is such a simple and fast side-dish to prepare that I make it regularly in the summer. It is especially good when accompanying a rice entree.

Basil Herbal Vinegar

Heat three cups of **white wine vinegar** (or champagne vinegar if you can find it) until just warm in a non-aluminum pan. Place one cup of torn **Opal Basil leaves**, stems and flowers in a clean one quart bottle. Add two thin strips of **orange or lemon zest**. This is not the white, bitter rind, but the thin colored skin — it can be removed with a potato peeler. Using a small funnel, pour the warm vinegar over the bottle contents and place a stopper or cork in the top. (Don't use a metal cap.) Set on a sunny window sill for five to six weeks (less if it's very warm weather). At the end of six weeks, pour the vinegar into a bowl through a sieve or cheesecloth to catch the herbs and zest. A chopstick can come in handy if they don't come out readily. Press all of the liquid from the herbs and zest into the vinegar. Rinse the bottle and return the vinegar through a funnel again. Add a new fresh sprig of basil if you wish and cork the bottle.

This vinegar will be a lovely shade of pink/violet and lasts many months. It is excellent in salad dressings and for sweet-and-sour red cabbage and marinades. Try it also sprinkled on a fresh melon salad.

Tomato & Basil Soup

Core two pounds of ripe, pear-shaped, **Roma tomatoes** (don't peel) and cut into chunks. Place in a three to four quart pan with two tablespoons of **olive oil** and one quarter cup fresh clean **basil leaves.** Cook, stirring occassionally, over medium-high heat until tomatoes mash easily — about 10-15 minutes. Pour into a blender and add one half cup each of hot **chicken broth** (homemade and unsalted) and **whipping cream** (or half-and-half). Whirl until pureed. Season with a little **salt and pepper.** Serve hot with one quarter cup chopped basil over the top or chill overnight and serve cold. Makes four one-cup servings.

This is a soup with an extraordinary flavor, freshly made, and so easy to do in about 20 minutes! I serve it many times during the basil season.

Cinnamon Basil Sauce For Fruit

Scoop one cup plain **low-fat yogurt** into a strainer lined with damp cheesecloth and let the liquid drain. In a small saucepan, bring ten **Cinnamon Basil leaves,** the juice of one half **lemon** and two tablespoons of **honey** just to a boil. Turn off the heat, let set 10-15 minutes, and then remove the basil. In a serving bowl, whisk drained yogurt with honey mixture until smooth. Cut the zest from the lemon in very thin strips and stir into the mixture. Serve over raspberries, strawberries, melon balls or all of the above. Makes about one cup.

This is a simple sauce to make and lasts a few days in the refrigerator.

 Other Notes

Usually three or four plants will produce enough fresh basil for a small family for the year. If you harvest and preserve an ample amount for winter's use, however, you will need about a dozen plants. One plant each of Holy Basil, Opal Basil, along with Lemon, Licorice or Cinnamon Basil, and several Sweet Basil plants will help you to experiment with the variety of tastes and colors that basil offers.

I usually grow a whole packet of seeds of Sweet Basil for preserving frozen leaves and making *pesto* sauce. I also grow seven or eight other varieties for color in the garden and for a wide range of uses in the kitchen and decorative uses. I hope you will enjoy growing your own basil and use it regularly during its short productive season.

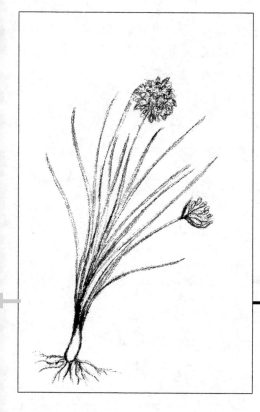

Chives

King of Oniondom

Chives

T he herb that most baked potato enthusiasts adore and the 'king of oniondom!' I have included chive in this book because of its great versatility. It is good with all kinds of foods, except desserts — and maybe there are some of these I don't know about. Chive flavor has been described as a sweet platonic onion with the echo of very young garlic, and is ideal for refined palates and delicate foods. Also following is some information on a few other members of the onion family that I particularly admire — and use intensively!

 Botanical Name

Members of the _Liliaceae family_, alliums are perennial plants and include garlic, chives, onions, and ornamental onions.

Chives — _Allium schoenoprasum_ — is the commonest form of chive found in most herb gardens and one of the first plants to show its leaves in the spring.

Garlic Chives — *Allium tuberosum* — has a number of common names including Oriental Garlic or Chinese Chives (gow choy). More on Garlic Chives later.

Egyptian Topping Onions — *Allium cepa Proliferum* — have leaves that are more onion-like, thick and round with hollow stems. They produce clumps of bulblets instead of seeds at the tops of the plants. The stems on these plants fall over, due to the weight, and as soon as they hit the ground they take root and become invasive if not thinned. They are quite flavorful and may be used like green scallions. This onion is probably the most ornamental in the garden because of its unusual growing habit.

Rocambole — *Allium sativum var. ophioscordon* — is also known as "serpent garlic" and is a topping garlic with purple-skinned bulblets. Its flat reed-like leaves resemble garlic chives except they are wider. The stems will often loop when they shoot up, thus the nickname, "serpent garlic." The bulbs are used like garlic and the stems or leaves like chives. It reproduces well once established.

Society Garlic — *Tulbaghia violacea* — is an attractive ornamental plant from South Africa and only grows native in that country. It is a tender perennial in Western Washington. Each plant has only five or six leaves with each leaf about a foot long. It is usually found growing in clumps. Although grown mostly for its ornamental effect, the leaves are tasty when chopped like chives. The flowers are lovely and bloom throughout both the summer and fall in the shape of stars. These are handsome when used to garnish platters. A 'tricolor' Society Garlic has variegated leaves in shades of green, white and pink. This plant lends beauty and interest when planted in a border or randomly amongst flowers and vegetables.

All of these chives are members of the lily family. With a variety of chive plants in your garden, you can have fresh chives year around. I have concentrated, however, on the first two....common chives and garlic chives.

History

Chives are native to Greece, Sweden, the Alps, and parts of Northern Britain. Also native to the Orient, they were probably first used by the Chinese 5,000 years ago and then brought to Greece. A thousand years before Christ was born, the Egyptian pharaohs fed their slaves and laborers large quantities of garlic (from the chive and onion family) in the belief that it would make them strong enough to build the pyramids. Chives have been a staple of European herb gardens since the sixteenth century.

When the Colonists came to America, they brought chive plants along with their other kitchen and medicinal herbs. They have continued to be one of the most popular and utilized herbs in American kitchens since those early days.

TYPE: Perennial *(except as noted)*

A perennial is a plant that endures winter cold and comes back from its roots each season to send up shoots and eventually flowers and seeds. A tender (or half-hardy) perennial is a plant which is marginally hardy in one's geographical location. These plants frequently will not survive a cold winter, although it is possible to pull them through a winter if well mulched. Chives, however, are hardy; and in our moderately mild Pacific Northwest, they weather the winter season well.

Description

These early spring rising allium plants are considered by some to be the "lilies of the kitchen" — along with their family mates of garlic, leeks and onions.

Like all onions, chives are bulb plants, although the bulbs are so tiny you may not realize they are there. The grass-like, hollow, green leaves and the flowering stems shoot up from the bulbs. The leaves are very slender, cylindrical, taper to a point at the tip and are from 6-10 inches long. Garlic chives will grow a bit taller, to about 14-18 inches tall and have flat green leaves about one quarter inch wide.

The chives begin flowering in June and continue for several weeks. The flower heads are small, round and pale mauve. They form dense globular umbels at the top of the stem. Garlic chives produce a lovely white, starry flower head that is looser than the lavender/pink ones of the onion chives. They begin blooming later in the summer. These two-inch flower heads have a wonderfully tangy taste.

Chives are tidy evergreen plants and are relatively maintenance free. All chives grow nicely in a clumping arrangement and do not spread (darn, I wouldn't mind having a few more 'volunteer,' like my potatoes). I will explain how to gain more plants, however, in the Propagation section.

Planting & Care Requirements

Chives prefer a light, rich, damp (though well-drained) soil with a pH 6.0. Coffee grounds make a good mulch for chives since they produce some acidity. The chives are nitrogen-loving plants which prefer full sun in which to develop their full fragrance and robust flavor. They will also tolerate some afternoon shade, however. They grow well in moist pastures and along stream banks. The plant can accept and even thrive in a variety of soil, moisture, and light conditions.

Chives will grow continuously if kept damp. If the leaves dry out, however, they will turn yellow and wilt. Yellowing of the leaves can also be caused by lack of nutrients — especially nitrogen. During a warm summer, chives are the one herb in my garden that I need to water manually (as opposed to letting Mother Nature do her thing.) However, too damp a soil causes root disease, which is why they need good drainage. Chives may also sustain some pest damage from slugs or snails. When planted near roses, however, chives act as a deterrent to the aphid pests because these pests prefer the chive plant to the roses.

Another way to use chives as a deterrent to insects is to utilize an abundance of chive leaf clippings as a mulch around each plant in your rose garden. Many obnoxious critters will be deterred with this application. Since I do not yet have an abundance of chive plants, I do not use this method, but intend to do so around my roses when my supply increases.

Chives are relatively maintenance free except for dead-heading the flowers. I usually remove the chive flower heads as soon as they begin to blossom. The Garlic Chive blossoms should be removed as the seeds turn from green to black, unless you desire a mass of Garlic Chives the following year. If you wish to keep the flavor in the leaves, you must remove the flowers when they appear and before they have fully opened. Save these flower heads for other uses. More about what to do with the flowers later.

All chive varieties make good edging or ornamental plants. As a mid-high border, randomly planted amongst flower beds or clustered together with other herbs, they create a charming effect.

Chives are also excellent container and indoor plants. They are sometimes planted in a single large pot along with parsley, basil and/or summer savory. As long as the soil is rich and well-drained and fed at regular intervals, they will thrive in these containers. If chives are raised in containers, the plants need a liquid feed (such as a fish fertilizer) every 14 days so the tops don't turn brown. Regular feedings of dried manure, fish emulsion or compost will help supply the nitrogen they need. The indoor container plants can become root-bound quite rapidly and will then need to be divided. See the section on Propagation for ways to do this division.

I have my chive plants as close as possible to the back door near my kitchen because I'm out cutting them every couple of days during the growing season. Chives keep their neat appearance throughout the spring, summer and fall with a minimum of care.

Harvesting

When harvesting chives, it's essential to cut the desired amount about one to two inches above ground level. Don't mow down the entire clump as the plant needs some of its leaves in order to keep producing. **Never top the plants,** in a haircut style, as this will stunt further growth and slow down your production as well as create dry ends. After cutting the desired amount of chives, I rinse them lightly (if they are dusty, otherwise I don't bother) and lay the bunch on paper toweling. Be sure to check among the leaves for any small bugs that may be hiding and eliminate them.

My usual method of mincing herbs is to tear them, but with chives I have never found a way to do this neatly or to cut chives quickly and efficiently with a knife. Instead, I hold the bunch by the middle and start snipping my way to the center. I then turn them around and snip from the other end to the center. I like using kitchen poultry shears for this, or better yet, my husband, Charles, does the cutting and snipping. That's the most efficient way of all! This is the same way I cut chives for all uses as it keeps them in nice little pieces rather than mushed up in a food processor or blender. I always start cutting chives when they are four to five inches tall so they will keep producing — with enough water, remember.

It takes a chive plant several years to become a full-grown, mature adult that produces leaves that are firm, hollow and thick. The smaller plants, however, have a more delicate taste. Some people let their chive heads form for the beautiful plant it makes. These can be left in the garden or used in floral arrangements...honest they look great, and their fragrance (odor) doesn't overwhelm the other cut flowers or herbs. My friend, Sue O'-Donnell, has many large, beautiful chive plants in her garden. They always flower because she doesn't cut or cook with them, but they are wonderful to see in her border mix with other flowers and plants. I hope that now, after reading my book, she will change her mind and serve at least a few on a dinner plate!

Preservation

Chives are best frozen, much like basil mentioned above. They can be dried, but commercially freeze-dried chives remain green while losing much of their flavor. Home-dried chives, unfortunately, are much like tasteless straw, if you are accustomed to the wonderful peppery taste of fresh chives.

To freeze the chives, I cut and snip as described above in harvesting and place the pieces in a freezer container. This can be a freezer zip-lock type bag (with all air removed) or a plastic or glass container. Again, use a container just large enough to hold the amount of chives with little air space remaining. This will discourage ice crystals from forming and the flavor deteriorating. I have recently purchased a food-sealing machine that does a wonderful job of sealing and vacuum packaging herbs for the freezer.

Instead of clipping the chive leaves before freezing, you may want to try bunching them into small logs instead. These 'logs' can be snipped frozen as you use them. Frozen chives can be used all winter long if you are lucky enough to keep them that long. My supply never lasts past Christmas no matter how many I freeze!

Chives can be chopped and frozen in ice cubes as explained with the basil. These can be frozen for over a year, but, of course, mine never stay around that long so I can't speak to the quality. It's really wonderful to have fresh, frozen chives in January on a baked potato.

If you wish to try dehydrating chives and tasting the results, follow the same procedure for harvesting and cleaning. Snip right onto trays or dry whole and snip them as you need them. When cleaning the chives you might find several that are brown and withered instead of green and fragrant. I usually pick these out by hand and toss them away. This is caused by having the chives get too dry or suffering a lack of nutrients.

As the summer wanes, your plants will produce less, so cut and harvest regularly (every few days) while they are at their peak, from June to September. If I followed my own advice and harvested regularly, I would probably have an ample supply preserved for the winter months. Maybe this year.

Propagation

Chives can be started from seed in the fall or early spring but they germinate very slowly (about two to three weeks) and require darkness, moisture and a constant temperature of about 60-70° F. Several seeds may be planted per four-inch pot and once the seedlings are a few inches high, be sure to keep them moist at all times. At this size they may be transplanted into the garden and thinned to 12 inches apart.

Although chives can be grown from seeds, it's much quicker and successful to divide established plants in the spring or autumn and transplant these divisions. Lift the entire plant with a garden fork and divide the clumps into smaller plants. You should lift and divide these clumps every three or four years for best ongoing production. If your chive clumps are large (eight or more inches in diameter), cut the leaves down to within an inch or two of ground level before lifting the plants with a fork or shovel. This helps to balance the tops of the plants with the amount of root-ball that will be lost in transplanting. With this top harvest gone, it alerts the plant to produce again after transplanting. Some fertilizer at this stage after replanting is very helpful for a fast recovery.

Another advantage of removing the whole plant from the ground to divide it, is to get a good look at the entire root-ball. If it is quite dense and compact, it can be aerated by pulling apart slightly or even cutting into the ball with a sharp knife if needed. If you simply dig up half the plant and replant in another area, you may not be solving the initial problem, which could be root-bound bulblets.

Propagation of Garlic Chives is very similar. You may leave the small black seeds in the garlic flower heads to dry and scatter on the ground. They will gladly self-sow. The rooted rhizomes will spread and become invasive if not controlled. If you prefer to contain your Garlic Chives, you can cut the flower heads and collect the seeds to give to friends. If you wish to divide the plant in the fall and pot up a clump about four inches in size, you will have a wonderful winter plant for fresh clipping indoors. Follow instructions under Other Notes in caring for these plants.

Culinary Uses

Chives have found a niche in all cuisines of the Northern Hemisphere, though they are used differently according to the taste and genus of each and depending on the creativity of the chef.

In Japanese food, chives are often a contrasting garnish for clear delicate soups. Russians favor them with fermented creams and milks and with beets and lamb. The Italians use them exclusively in summer green salads. The French have an affinity for chives with egg dishes, light sauces, and lightly cooked vegetables. The French also combine them with shallots, marjoram, and tarragon as a complement to many dishes. The English use of chives is concentrated on fresh cheeses and salads. The German cooks use them in mayonnaise and *remoulades*. Egyptians and Lebanese garnish spicy meat stews and sauces with chives. Persian cuisine uses chives and Garlic Chives lavishly in herb salads, meat sauces and soups. In the United States, we mostly use them for baked potatoes. That is now about to change.

Usually chives are used in a 'raw' state as they lose much of their flavor and nutritional value when cooked. Chive blossoms are especially good sprinkled on omelettes and other egg dishes, sometimes in combination with tarragon. Tangy and tasty chive heads can be used in salads but be sure to separate the tiny petals (and I remove the stem) as they are a whopping surprise if a dinner guest gets a full chive head in a forkful of salad. The blossoms are pretty to scatter on top of soup as well, especially a potato soup. I use them in combination with other ingredients to create chicken, beef and vegetable broths as well. My favorite recipe for using chive heads, however, is in vinegar as explained in the Recipe section. The lavender blossoms are wonderful in white wine vinegar creating a lovely pink and appetizing vinegar for many uses!

The attractive Garlic Chive blossoms can be dipped in a light batter like *Tempura* and fried gently until golden brown...an exceptional and rare treat! Garlic Chives are nice in herb butters, too, and try sprinkling them on meat just before it's removed from the grill.

Chive leaves can, of course, be chopped and used in all of these ways as well. Like most herbs, the whole chive plant is edible. This includes the leaves and flower heads, as well as the bulbs. The bulbs can be pickled, although I have not tried this.

Chives are wonderful on most vegetables, especially peas, carrots, and tomatoes. I also add them to creamy sauces at the end of the cooking time for poultry. Garnishing an entree with long chive leaves and blossoms makes an attractive presentation. I do not, however, like the *stems* of the Garlic Chives that hold the white, starry flower heads. These stems get very stiff early in the season when they produce the flowers. These stiff stems are few, however, and can actually be used in floral arranging or as skewers for very soft foods like tomatoes, mushrooms, or olives. If used as skewers, leave the lovely white floral heads attached. The flat garlic leaves without the flower heads are supple, piquant, and of course, garlicky-tasting.

Medicinal Uses

Although medicinal virtues have been found in most herbs, herbalists do not find much use for chives, unlike their relative, the garlic. It was once thought that chives could drive away diseases and evil influences, probably because of the pungent aroma. Bunches of chives were hung in the home for this purpose. Even if they didn't protect the home from these intruders, the dried flowers added beauty for decorative purposes.

Chives send up hot vapors from a sulfur-rich oil found in all members of the onion genus. This oil is also responsible for the flavor and medicinal properties of alum. Sulfur oil is antiseptic and helps lower blood pressure, but only if used in fairly large quantities. Chives have been known to act as a laxative when drunk as a tea.

All allium — garlic, onion, chives — are found to be a blood cleanser when barely cooked. Chive leaves are generally less irritating to the digestive tract than onion or garlic bulbs so many people prefer them in their recipes.

 ## Other Uses

Garlic Chive stems with the flowers are lovely in floral arrangements or with other herbs in arrangements at individual place settings. These floral heads are also attractive on wreath arrangements. The delicate white clusters of starry flowers on the Garlic Chives dry to rice-paper translucence. The small black seeds can be clearly seen in the inside.

Any leftover chive bulbs can be pickled in white wine vinegar for a refreshing winter taste. These are said to be wonderful with cold meats, especially roast beef.

When recipes call for scallions, the green leaf part of the chive can be used as a substitute. If planted near roses or tomatoes, the chive plants deter Japanese beetles from the area, as well as being the aphid deterrent mentioned earlier.

 ## Recipes

Chive Butter

Soften eight tablespoons (one quarter pound) of **unsalted butter.** Add three tablespoons of chopped **chive leaves**, or a combination of leaves and flowers, and mix well (with the back of a wooden spoon). This can be prepared in a food processor as well. Beat in one tablespoon of fresh squeezed **lemon juice** and one-eighth teaspoon of ground **white pepper**. Chill in two or three tartlet pans. Remove the shaped butters from the pans when they are firm, and freeze in plastic bags until ready to use.

This can also be made in one-half to one pound portions, rolled into a cylinder and cooled in parchment or plastic wrap. To use, unwrap, slice coins of one quarter inch off the butter as needed, rewrap the remainder and freeze. Try these butter coins on broiled fish of all kinds as well as to top a special beef steak. This butter can be kept in the refrigerator for several weeks or frozen for longer periods of time.

Chive & Cucumber Juice

Cut one and one half large (unpeeled) **cucumbers** into chunks and put through a juice extractor. Mix in one cup of un-flavored **yogurt** and stir in one and one half tablespoons of chopped **chives.** Mix and serve. Makes four small glasses as a morning pick-me-up or as an appetizer for dinner. This recipe is a little different, and a nutritious light, eye-opener.

Tomato Sauce With Chives

Sauté one or two cloves of chopped **garlic** in two teaspoons of **olive oil.** Add one pint of **cherry tomatoes,** stems removed (or two large tomatoes coarsely chopped). Contine to sauté for two or three minutes and toss with two tablespoons of fresh **chopped chives.** Remove from the heat and serve over pasta, cooked chicken breasts or steamed fish (halibut). This is wonderfully easy to prepare and so low in calories!

Green Rice With Chives *(An Italian Dish)*

In a two-quart saucepan, add two tablespoons **olive oil** and four tablespoons **butter.** Add three quarter cups each of fresh cut **chives,** chopped **parsley,** and fresh **spinach,** finely chopped. Cover and cook over low heat for five minutes. Add two cups of **short-grain rice** (not the instant kind) and cook until translucent. Add two cups of hot **chicken stock** (preferably homemade), one teaspoon **salt** and one quarter teaspoon **pepper.** Cover and cook over low heat. Add one and one half cups more **stock,** cover with a tight-fitting lid and cook for another ten minutes, or until rice is tender. Garnish with fresh grated **Parmesan, Romano or Pecorino Cheese.**

This is a wonderful accompaniment to pork or poultry. You may use frozen spinach and/or frozen chopped parsley, but the chives should be fresh for the best result.

 ## Other Notes

Chives are so beautiful and aromatic in the garden, they are worth growing for these reasons alone. Bees and butterflies also love them which is beneficial in turn to other plants nearby.

If using chives as an indoor plant, you may divide a clump from the garden in the fall and place one portion in a pot. After the leaves have died back from frost outside, bring the plant inside for the winter. It will make vigorous growth and may last several years indoors. If your potted plant becomes pot-bound (also known as root-bound) take it from the pot, pull apart into clumps about two to three inches in diameter and replant in separate pots filled with fresh potting medium (not garden soil). These indoor potted plants need a dormant period and, therefore, should be placed in a cooler, darker place than the sunny location they enjoyed outdoors. They may remain outdoors for dormancy if they do not freeze. A potted chive plant with an attached card of a few recipes makes a wonderful year-round gift for a gardener or cook.

Chives can make a natural insecticide when mixed with garlic and ground chili and added to water to spray on plants.

Garlic, shallots, scallions, leeks and elephant garlic can all be interchangeable in most recipes as well as wonderful companion plantings.

Chives are very nutritious and contain calcium, phosphorous, sulfur (a natural antibiotic), iron, vitamins A & C and pectin. Like the flavor, however, these nutrients are diminished by cooking.

I can't imagine an herb offering any more to us than chives...beautiful, easy to grow, nutritious, tasty and very aromatic. Try some this spring or fall.

Notes:

Lavender

My Grandmother's Fragrance

Lavender

D o all of us remember our grandmothers smelling of lavender fragrance, or is it just my memory? Many of our earliest childhood memories are of that lovely, fragrant toilet water.

In Tudor times, lavender stood for 'trust' and was a familiar sight in 'knot gardens' where the flower beds were laid out in geometric design and enclosed by low hedges. (Lavender makes a wonderfully scented hedge.) In those days, lavender was used extensively in cooking as well as in medicinal products.

In the language of herbs, lavender stands for luck, silence, sad refusal, or distrust.

Although lavender is more an ornamental herb used for crafts and decorative household items, medicinals and cosmetics today, I have included it because it is so recognized and loved by gardeners. I have also discovered several culinary uses as well. However, if you wish to grow this herb for its fragrance and beauty in the garden, without thought of ever harvesting it, I can surely understand that!

Botanical Name

There are at least 28 varieties of lavender in the genus *Lavandula,* and even horticulturists get confused. Some people choose lavender for their gardens based upon the flowering times; early (May or June), mid-summer (June or July), or late blooming summer (August and later).

English Lavender or True Lavender — Botanically there is no such name, but the familiar herb we know as this variety is *Lavandula angustifolia, Lavandula officinalis, Lavandula spica,* or *Lavandula vera.* English lavenders generally bloom first in the season. Other varieties of 'English Lavender' include the following:

'Munstead' — *Lavandula angustifolia 'Munstead'* * — is a semi-dwarf, smaller cushion-type lavender and usually a dark purple in color (my personal favorite). This gray-green plant grows 12-18" tall and has an especially sweet fragrance without medicinal overtones.

'Hidcote' — *L. angustifolia 'Hidcote'* — is short and hardy, very compact and free-flowering in a deep violet color. It usually grows less than one and one half feet high with stems and foliage in gray with a downy texture.

'Jean Davis' — *L. angustifolia 'Jean Davis'* — has pale pink to white blooms which is very unusual. This variety is very similar to 'Rosea' which has pink flowers.

Lavandin — *L. x intermedia* — is a hybrid cross between L. angustifolia and L. latifolia. This lavender is grown for its oil content, and these plants bloom a little later in the summer. Varieties include:

'Grosso' — *L. x intermedia 'Grosso'* — is a compact French variety that carries two foot long stems topped by oceans of dark blue flower spikes. It starts blooming on 14-24" spikes about June or July and should be planted 36" apart. Sometimes called 'Fat Spike' because of its huge dark violet flower heads, it is one of the largest of any lavender. This and similar hybrids in the Lavandin group are vigorous and more

---

*Lavandula angustifolia 'Munstead' does exist but is rare in cultivation. It is very dwarf, with blue foliage and rich purple flowers.

"evergreen" than any other hardy lavender. This plant is very fragrant with a fan-like blooming habit.

'Provence' — *L. x intermedia 'Provence'* — is a hardy plant with a very pleasant lavender fragrance and is not susceptible to fungus. The dark aster violet flowers bloom in mid-season and the plant is a robust grower. This variety has very long flower spikes which make it a good candidate for lavender fans and swags.

Tender lavenders include:

'Pinnata' — *L. pinata* — has leaves and flowers that are very fragrant and dry well. The leaves are lacy and a light gray-green in color.

Fern Leaf — *L. multifida* — makes a colorful and fragrant addition to a balcony garden. Soil mix should include some sand.

French or Spanish Lavender — *L. stoechas* — has light green, narrow foliage and very dark purple, dense flower heads. This delightful lavender has large purple bracts that protrude like wings from a small egg-shaped bud, giving the effect of a fat-bodied butterfly. Some people think they resemble little bunny ears. Usually growing no more than 12-18 inches tall, it's more tender than 'English' lavender and only suitable for areas with the mildest climates.

'Otto Quast' — *L. stoechas 'Otto Quast'* — grows one and one half to three feet tall. The flower bracts have cleverly shaped bunny ears and the flowers are fringed.

Green French — *L. dentata* — has fernlike, sawtooth foliage with blue flowers and gray or green leaves. Sometimes called Fringed-Leaf Lavender, the flowers appear around a green globe instead of clustering along a stem. This lavender does very well in container plantings and hanging baskets.

Woolly Lavender — *L. lanata* — lives up to its name by producing white, fuzzy, balsam-scented leaves along with compact purple-blue flower spikes.

Dwarf Lavender — *L. angustifolia 'Nana Alba'* — is a compact variety with spikes of white flowers one and one half to two inches long. It's very dainty and delicate looking.

Dwarf lavender — <u>*L. angustifolia*</u> *'Nana Atropurpurea'* — grows eight inches tall and 15-18" wide with dark purple flowers in early summer.

All lavenders are members of the mint family, Labiatae, having the square-shaped stems that make them recognizable in this vast family of plants.

 # History

The name lavender derives from the Latin verb, *lavare* or *lavage*, "to wash," and both the Romans and Greeks scented their soaps and bath water with this refreshing and fragrant herb.

We sometimes think of lavender associated with the English garden or, perhaps, the French Alps of Southern France where the hills are washed with color and scent. Lavender is native to the Mediterranean area but grown commercially in England and Southern France, especially Provence. Here it is grown in hot stony soils where it seems to thrive with neglect. I'm told by our daughter Julie, who recently visited the area, that the color and scent of lavender fields are dramatic and can be almost overwhelming to the nose on a breezy day.

In the Middle Ages, lavender was thought to be an herb of love. It was considered both an aphrodisiac to gain affection, and to keep the wearer chaste if lavender water was sprinkled on one's head. A dichotomy of uses perhaps, but it worked for them!

Lavender was indispensable to Victorian melodrama as it was an ingredient of 'aromatic spirits of ammonia' used to prevent fainting spells, or swooning. Tussie mussies (or nosegays) always included fragrant lavender as one of the herbal, aromatic ingredients. These groups of herbs were placed in elaborate gold or silver filigree holders and carried in the hand to ward off disease and counteract bad odors. (No chemical deodorants back then!) In England today, judges at Old Bailey, Britain's highest criminal court, still carry tussie mussies into the courtroom six times each year as a gesture to tradition. In China, lavender is used in a cure-all medicinal oil called White Flower Oil.

No lavenders are native to America, but they are naturalized in the southern United States as well as widely cultivated throughout the world.

 ## TYPE: Perennial

Although lavender is a fairly hardy perennial, it sometimes will not withstand severe winters. Depending upon the species and location of the plant(s), it will need some special care in colder climates. This perennial plant will grow for many years, but in order to obtain the fullest fragrance, individual plants are usually replaced every five years or so with new plants or by cuttings.

 ## Description

Lavender is a small evergreen shrub growing up to four feet high with square stems and leaves of whitish-gray. Flowers are from dark mauve to lighter shades of lavender, blue, pinks, and even white. The flowers are small, with a five-lobed corolla. Whorls of six to ten flowers form terminal spikes on six to eight inch stems. The leaves are opposite each other and smooth-edged, somewhat hairy, and usually silvery gray.

The plant flowers from May to September depending upon the variety. This is a bushy, branching shrub, and there are several sub-shrubs in the species. The stems of mature plants often become a dense, woody tangle.

This colorful herb is frequently grown as a fragrant low hedge, in which case it should be pruned hard in early spring, *almost* back to old wood.

In describing the flavor of lavender, my description is that it tastes just like it smells — does that make sense to you? If you smell the plant (flowers and stems as well) with your eyes closed, you can sense its uniquely sweet, floral flavor.

Planting & Care Requirements

To insure growing fragrant lavender successfully, the proper soil and pruning, along with patience will produce winning plants. A well-drained soil (non-acidic with lime) is necessary for successful growing. This well-drained soil can create a drought condition, however, in hot summer weather, so attention must be paid during this time to young plants so that they do not dry out. Lavender tolerates a much narrower pH range than many other herbs. A slightly alkaline soil of pH 7.1 is a perfect balance for lavender. It cannot withstand soils with acidity levels much below pH 6.5 or much above pH 8.5. Sulfur acidifies soil; lime raises pH. Poor growth and early death are sometimes the result of improper pH.

These plants benefit from a mulch of coarse sand one or two inches deep beneath the plants. This will increase growth and flower production and help fight fungal diseases that are inevitably fostered by hot, humid summers and damp winters. A mulch of sand around the base of the plants aids in growth and helps prevent winter damage. Sand and gravel are much to its liking. Clay soil should be amended with sand, some compost and a little lime when planting. Side dressings of manure or liquid fertilizer should be applied regularly until September if plants are grown outdoors. Too much water or too fertile a soil, however, will make the plant too bushy and produce less floral scent. When the plant is trying to avoid drought, it will produce its oils; therefore, dryness creates more scent. Most of the oil scent is in the bracts (these hold the blossoms) but there is some scent in the stems as well. *Scent is better in poorer soil with less water.*

All lavenders like a sunny sheltered location, especially as protection from strong winter winds. Even in summer storms, the spikes of flowers are easily broken. A lavender plant should not be encouraged to bloom in its first year. Constant pruning of the stems, to keep the plant from expending energy on flowers at this stage of early growth, is desirable since it keeps the plant's activity directed toward foliage and root production. The pruning also helps keep the plant compact and aids in the development of strong stems and good structure.

Lavender can be grown as a tallish ground cover in dry areas, as a specimen plant, or as a low hedge. Lavender thrives when grouped with other lavenders, but air circulation between the plants is a must. I plant mine two feet apart to allow for their spreading foliage. Planting on small mounds encourages good drainage for the plants. In addition to good drainage and air circulation, this herb does best in a warm sunny location. I grow eight varieties of lavender in an open garden with a southern exposure but with fence protection from the northern winds.

If the lower leaves turn brown or yellow, it indicates either too much moisture or crowding of the plant. Fungus diseases and caterpillars sometimes attack lavenders but routine care is minimal. By regularly pruning the plants, fungus disease will be discouraged. Shaping of the bushy plants can be done either after the flowering and harvesting lightly in the fall or in the early spring. Full pruning should only be done in the spring.

Lavender grows well in containers if the plants are set in coarse, porous soil. Water them infrequently and keep the winter night temperature range between 40° F. and 50° F., with daytime temperatures only 5-10° higher. Indoor-grown lavender needs good air circulation around it to keep the leaves from blackening. Select the tender varieties for indoor culture. Pot in a well-drained mixture such as peat moss and perlite in equal amounts with some lime added. Grow in a sunny spot and fertilize at least monthly. Take care with watering as too much water, especially with reduced light levels, will quickly cause lavender roots to rot. It is best to allow the growing medium to dry without permitting the plants to wilt. White flies may be a problem indoors but using an insecticidal soap spray will aid in control.

Try planting lavender on either side of a walkway so that when you sashay down the walk you will 'nudge' the plants and they will release their scent. Of course, if we all wore long skirts, this nudging would be a little easier. Lavender works well in garden borders, too, because of its clumping bush shape.

Lamb's Ear — <u>*Stachy byzantina*</u> — and lavender planted together make a wonderful color combination of silver/lavender. The Lamb's Ear will spread easily, however, so you must control its invasive nature. The flowers of the Lamb's Ear can be pruned, dried and used along with lavender in splendid floral arrangements and wreath construction. Other suggestions for companion plantings with lavender might include old shrub roses, dianthus, catmints, creeping thyme (Doone Valley) or hyssop.

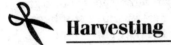

Harvesting

Harvest lavender in the early morning after the dew is gone but before the sun heats it up. For the best crop of lavender for bouquets, the stems may be picked as the last few buds are opening. For the most fragrant and longest-lasting scent, however, pick the stems when the buds are still tight and only the lower buds have popped open. These buds retain the potent and aromatic lavender oil and make excellent *potpourri,* wands or sachets. Cut the stems above the first leaves. An early picking in late May or June of the early blooming varieties sometimes provides a second flowering later in the summer. Early spring is a good time to shape the plant by cutting out old wood and trimming gangly branches. Remove half the length of each lavender stem to keep their size under control. This will reinvigorate and shape the plant as well as increase flower production.

Do not cut your lavender to the ground, particularly in the fall, as this can severely stunt its growth and it will probably not survive. It needs old wood to produce new stems. Lavender can be pruned back by one-third in the fall. The blooms, however, come on the new stems each year. Cutting up to one-half will not seriously injure the plant. The tops can be pinched for better branching. Lavender's fragrance peaks after three to five years and the plants should be replaced at that time for full potential as an aromatic herb.

After cutting, the buds (or flowers if they have opened) can be removed from each stem by using the forefinger and thumb of one hand, while you hold the stem in the other. Or whole stems can be picked and used fresh or dried. The dried stems (after flowers have been removed) can be gathered into bunches and tied with paper ribbon, or raffia. These can be used on a fire to give the room a pleasant lavender aroma or can be given as gifts. The stems of mints, thymes, rosemary and basils work well for this as well. Don't waste any of that lovely fragrance.

In the second to fifth years, full pickings of lavender are possible before replacing the plants — hopefully with new cuttings you have taken yourself. (See techniques in the Propagation section.)

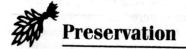 **Preservation**

Lavender can be preserved with the best results obtained by drying, and this can be done in several ways.

Gather lavender in bunches and dry hanging with the tops down. When hanging, secure each bundle with a rubber band encircling the stem ends so that, as the stems dry and shrink, the band tightens with them keeping them secure. Twist-ems or ties work well at first, but tend to loosen as the herbs dry. An easy hanger can be made from a large paper clip opening up to an "S" shape. The location for drying these bunches is *very* important. An attic or a hot, dry, upstairs room usually works well. Avoid basements if there is any dampness. A garage can be used; however, if a car is parked in the garage, herbs should be placed in paper bags, with holes for moisture escape, to prevent fumes and dust from settling on the leaves. To preserve the color, lavender should be dried in a *dark place, and as rapidly as possible.*

Lavender flowers or buds can also be dried on screens in a dehydrator either on or off the stems. I prefer to dry mine on the stems and remove the small buds or flowers later for use in *potpourri* or in cooking. The removal of the buds or flower blossoms after drying is easier to accomplish than when they are fresh. The dried stems then are ready for bundling for my fireplace or barbecue grill. See the notes on preservation under basil in Chapter One for layout and drying times.

Lavender can also be dried in an oven or outdoors in the open air (never in the sun), but I find hanging the bundles upside down to be the superior method if you don't have a dehydrator.

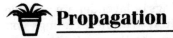 **Propagation**

Propagation by seed is not the most successful way of increasing your lavender supply. *'Munstead'* lavender seed is available, however, and easy to grow in this way. The seeds need a germination temperature of 70° F. and can be covered or uncovered. This germination should take from five to ten days. If you choose to propagate in this way, be sure to plant when the seeds will be chilled in the earth for two to four weeks, with a warming time to follow. That's pretty hard to predict — at least here in my neighborhood!

Cuttings can be either a heel cutting or tip cutting. A four-inch cutting from the best stems will produce roots most quickly. To take a heel cutting, grasp a healthy shoot and pull it downward so that a piece of the older wood comes along with it as it breaks off. Strip the lowest leaves from the cutting and pinch off any buds or flowers near the bottom. Dip the bare root end into hormone rooting powder (like Rootone) if you wish, and insert each cutting about an inch deep and three to four inches apart in moist, sandy soil with perlite in a shaded cold frame or in pots. When set in sand in summer in this way, they will root by late autumn and be ready for planting in open ground by the following spring.

For a tip cutting, simply cut the top four to six inches from a healthy stem, remove any lower leaves and proceed as above. Water these small pots and place in a semi-shady area. As fall and colder temperatures arrive place in a more protected location.

Lavender may also be propagated by mound layering. This can be done by mounding garden soil up beyond the roots of the lavender plant until it reaches a few inches up the stems. New roots will develop on these buried stems that are further up from the first set of roots in the soil. If you mound the soil in spring, check the new roots by uncovering a section in early fall. If the roots are developed you can cut that stem section off and repot for a new lavender plant. The advantage of cuttings or mound layering is to produce an identical plant, a clone, of the one you have in your garden.

To keep these new plants from flowering and to encourage branching into lateral shoots, the new growth on these plants should be clipped as it appears.

Culinary Uses

Although lavender is more noted for use in decorative and cosmetic products, I have gathered together a number of culinary uses as well. I have tried several of these on trusting friends and family members and they seem to love the flavor. Remember it tastes just like it smells! Who could resist experimenting with the flavor? As a general rule, use the darker flowers for eating.

The flowers or buds can be used in tea which is usually taken medicinally. But a refreshing tea can be steeped for drinking with Lemon Verbena and served over ice; sort of a lavender-lemon ice-ade. A delicate, quenching lemonade in the summer is delightful and I have given you the recipe for this favorite beverage below. If making a "brew" of lavender flower heads, remember that it can be quite potent and disagreeable to some. Better to serve as above over ice.

Lavender flowers make a nice sprinkle or garnish for desserts. Use these flowers sparingly in custards, puddings, and with fruit and all sorts of berries. The flowers additionally may be used in jams and vinegars. Try them sprinkled on salads of greens or fruits for a great taste treat and a lovely mauve color. The dried stems of lavender (with or without the buds attached) make good skewers for desserts spiked through fresh fruit pieces. I've used these with melon, berries, banana and pineapple. A lovely lavender ice cream is served at The Herbfarm in Fall City, Washington, and since their recipe is a secret, I have given you my recipe below.

My favorite lavender recipe, and my husband's (the lover of pork!), is an herb mix that is used as a dry marinade. See that recipe below for a remarkable flavor with all kinds of meats...especially Charlie's pork roast.

The famous dried herb blend of French chefs, *'Herbes de Provence'*, contains a mixture of lavender blossoms, thyme, savory, basil, and fennel, and can be used on all sorts of meat and fish as well as in sauces and on pizza. Lavender herb butter combined with dried rosemary is splendid on biscuits or in making cookies. Dried or fresh flowers can also be ground or powdered and used in this same manner. Even the bitter leaves and tips of the plant can be enjoyed in soups, vinegars, jellies, and wine.

In making herbal jellies I sometimes add a sprig of lavender to each jar. My favorite is raspberry jelly or jam with a lavender sprig — for a new taste and an unusual gift.

Although lavender vinegar can be made easily, it is more usually found on the dressing table than the dinner table. More on cosmetic uses to follow.

 Medicinal Uses

Lavender is used as a 'modest' medicinal herb as well as a 'modest' culinary herb.

Until World War I, lavender was mostly used as a disinfectant for wounds and has been used as an ingredient for smelling salts.

Lavender aroma balances moods in acting as a stimulant or a sedative. This herb seems to reverse the mood when inhaled.

The lighter the color of lavender flowers (from white to pink), the more stimulant. The darker the flowers (from blue to lavender), the more sedative. If agitated, it will calm; if lethargic, it will stimulate. Many naturopathic physicians use lavender in their waiting rooms for this purpose, and aromatherapy is becoming very popular. What a great 'drug' — a natural relaxant for sleep or picker-upper to inspire. Lavender is very safe to use, like rose and chamomile flowers.

Headaches and 'giddiness' can be relieved by a cold lavender compress to the forehead. (See the glossary for instructions on this.) A hot lavender tea can be drunk for flatulence and dizziness as well as for halitosis. I certainly can understand why lavender is a remedy for halitosis with its wonderfully penetrating aroma.

Lavender is also anti-bacterial in a lotion-type solution of lavender flowers steamed in water, especially when used on cuts, burns, and bug bites. These antibacterial properties are possibly due to the volatile oil which contains camphor. I have listed a preparation for an anti-bacterial ointment in the recipe section that is very easy to make. Eczema and psoriasis, two skin conditions, can be helped by drops of lavender oil in a hot bath. When used as an infusion, lavender is also good for sprains, muscular pain and stiffness.

An infusion can be made by placing leaves, flowers and stems in a soft, clean cloth (or use dried) and 'bruise' lightly with the heel of the hand to extract the healing juices. Put three tablespoons of fresh, or one tablespoon of dried, herbs in a warm bowl and cover with two and one half cups of boiling water. Cover tightly and let stand four to six minutes. Strain and it's ready to use. Infusions are best used hot or cold when they are fresh.

? Other Uses

Lavandin oil is a precious commodity, and is used in the finest French perfumes. This perfume requires fifty pounds of lavandin flowers to produce one pound of essential oil — or one acre of lavandin, in a good year, yields 15-20 pounds of oil. Distilled lavandin oil is aged for several months before being sold.

Before the marvels of current cosmetics, lavender was used as a skin tonic (especially as an anti-wrinkle solution because it promotes new skin growth). It is currently used in cosmetics for foot baths, skin toners, facial steams, and hair rinses as well as being beneficial as a topical application for blemishes when made into a lotion. This wonderfully fragrant herb stimulates and cleanses the skin with an astringent action. A lavender herb water is a superb after-shave lotion for men (or women too, I suppose). A lavender vinegar recipe is offered below for your consideration as a skin toner.

For room fragrance, place one tablespoon lavender flowers in a bowl of hot water and stir. The leaves and stems can be used in *potpourris*, dried floral arrangements, and sleep pillows (remember it promotes relaxation when agitated). The *'Jean Davis'* variety is a good choice for a room freshener if you wish stimulation, or *'Hidcote'* for relaxation.

A lavender-rose *potpourri* can be made from one tablespoon each of dried spearmint, basil, and rose petals with one cup of lavender flowers. Add some grated, dried lemon peel and two tablespoons of Sweet Woodruff as a fixative.

A good friend, Virginia Terrell, is an expert lavender grower and user. She makes little lavender-colored cloth bags and encloses dried lavender buds and one half of a dryer softener (like Bounce). After stitching the bags closed, they are used in the clothes dryer to soften as well as give a great fragrance to her lingerie. What a great idea. Another idea from Virginia is to fill a lovely little basket or china bowl with dried lavender buds and place on the bathroom counter. When family or guests, wash and dry their hands, they can do a final 'rinse' in the finger bowl with dried lavender for a lovely enduring fragrance.

Dried lavender buds enclosed in muslin bags set among your clothes drawers and closets make an excellent moth repellent as well as fragrant sachet. The same moth repellency effect is achieved in the garden when lavender is planted, in addition to spurning flies and mosquitos.

This multi-purpose herb is also used in decorative wreath-making, sprays, and other floral arrangements. Although I grow several lavender plants a year, I never have enough for all of these lovely uses.

 # Recipes

Lavender Ice Cream

Combine one half cup of **lavender flowers** and three cups of **milk** and heat to *just* boiling. Remove from heat and allow the mixture to sit for ten minutes. Meanwhile, combine one cup **sugar** with six **egg yolks** and whip to a smooth consistency. Strain the milk into the egg-yolk mixture, stirring constantly. Discard the flowers. Cook this combination until it is steaming hot and slightly thickened but has not yet begun to boil. Quickly remove from heat and allow to cool. Stir in three cups of **heavy cream** and chill. Freeze in an ice cream freezer.

Lavender Herb Mix *(For Pork Roast)*

To make one cup of herb mix, combine one quarter cup each of dried **lavender flowers** and whole dried **oregano leaves**; two tablespoons each of whole dried **fennel seeds** and whole dried **rosemary leaves**; one tablespoon each of dried **thyme leaves** and dried **sage leaves**. Combine well and store in an airtight jar. This will keep for at least a year if kept covered in a cool, dry place.

To prepare a marinade for roast pork, crush and rub one or two tablespoons of mix (depending on size of roast) on all surfaces of meat. Chill, covered overnight. Roast slowly on a lower rack in the oven at 300° F. in a pan with a little water in the bottom until inside temperature reaches 170° F. Let set 10 minutes before carving. Degrease broth in pan bottom and deglaze pan with a little white wine. Drizzle over pork after slicing.

Luscious Lavender Lemonade

Pour one cup boiling water over four tablespoons of **lavender flowers or buds** and allow to steep for ten minutes. Strain out the flowers and add one cup **sugar** and juice from three **lemons** to the water. Stir in one quart of **sparkling water** and chill.

An even easier way to make 'luscious lavender lemonade' is to use a commercial lemonade and add the steeped, strained lavender infusion. Mix, chill and enjoy! I like to serve this with Lemon Balm or Lemon Verbena leaves floating in the glass or frozen into the ice cubes.

Lavender Sugar

Use a clean pint jar with a tight-fitting lid. Fill the jar about one-third full with **sugar,** and scatter a small handful of **lavender flowers** over it. (Sugar can be made extra fine by running through a kitchen processor.) Cover the flowers with sugar so that the jar is two-thirds full, add another small handful of flowers, leaving about one half inch head space. Put on the lid, shake the jar, and place it on a shelf in a cool, dark place. You may remove the flowers by sifting the sugar through a colander if you wish. Place a soda cracker in the jar to keep the sugar from accumulating moisture. The sugar will be ready to use in two to three weeks but will become more flavorful with age. As you use the sugar in cookies, cakes, biscuits, or lemonade, add more sugar and it will take on the same fragrance and taste in the jar.

Lavender Ointment

You may use pure lard or white petroleum jelly (Vaseline) in this recipe. If using **lard,** slowly heat eight ounces in a pan until melted and add one ounce of crushed **lavender buds** or flowers. Stir until it boils and then simmer for 30 minutes. Strain into small jars and cover when they are cold. With **petroleum jelly,** use one ounce of crushed **flowers or buds** to four ounces of jelly and simmer for only 20 minutes.

This ointment stores for many months and can be used very successfully on cuts, scrapes, abrasions, burns and other minor injuries. I find it very healing and soothing when I sustain cuts and blisters working in my gardens.

Lavender Vinegar *(A lovely cosmetic)*

Warm one pint of **cider vinegar** in a non-aluminum pan. Pour over one quarter cup each of fresh **lavender flowers** and **mint leaves.** Let steep on a warm window sill for three to four weeks. Strain the flowers and leaves out of the vinegar and press any liquids from the flowers before discarding. Return vinegar to a sterilized bottle and keep on your dressing table. To use as a facial toner dilute one part lavender vinegar with six parts of soft water. As a bath additive, pour three to four tablespoons into a warm bath and luxuriate.

Lavender Potpourri

In a large bowl, mix together one cup of **dried lavender flowers,** two cups of dried **Lemon Verbena leaves,** one tablespoon each of **whole cloves, cinnamon pieces,** and **whole allspice,** and two tablespoons of dried **Sweet Woodruff or Orris Root Powder.** Add a few drops of **lavender essential oil** to prolong the fragrance. Store in a tightly closed glass or ceramic jar. Use in bags for drawer fresheners, in an open bowl to fragrance the air, or in small jars with holes in them for ongoing bouquet.

 Other Notes

Lavender wands or bottles made by weaving ribbons with the stems is a popular way of preserving lavender and to give as gifts. Further information on how to do this can be obtained from the *Herb Companion Magazine,* April/May of 1992 or other sources. I have tried this many times and have found that my fingers do not want to do what my mind says needs to be done to create these lovely, aromatic wands. Virginia Terrell's are great — I think she has much more patience than I do and probably more dexterity as well.

In warmer latitudes, entire road sides are blanketed with lavender for beautification and soil stabilization.

Dried powdered lavender can be brushed into pet fur to deter 'critters'. My dog, Taffy, not only likes the fragrance, but she enjoys the process of incorporating this herb in her fur. And, yes, it really does work. If you live in Bambi country, browsing deer will not touch lavender, making it an ideal landscape plant or border to a vegetable garden.

Dried lavender leaves, stems, or flowers may be sewn into small bags to be used as 'moth chasers' in your closets.

Don't confuse Lavender Cotton with the herbal lavender plant I have described. Lavender Cotton is a santolina which, in fact, is a member of the daisy family.

Would you believe that this herb has also been used for embalming corpses, curing animals of lice, taming lions and tigers, and as a flavoring for snuff and other aromatic tobaccos? One variety has also been used in varnish and lacquers, especially those used on porcelain. My, my! What some people find to do with this wonderful herb! Try it, I know you will love it, too.

Lavender really is a must for any herb garden.

Lemon Balm

The Children's Herb

Lemon Balm

T here are numerous lemon-scented herbs that are well worth growing in your herb garden. Some of my favorites, and ones that I have successfully grown, are Lemon Thyme, Lemon Mint, Lemon Verbena and Lemon Basil. Others that I have not yet tried include Lemon Grass, Lemon Gem Marigold and Lemon Catnip. From this beginning list you can see that lemon is a fragrance found in several different varieties of herb plants.

Perhaps the best-known lemon herb and my personal favorite is Lemon Balm. There are two particular reasons that I prefer Lemon Balm: first, children love to put their faces and hands in the plant and enjoy its citrus aroma; and secondly, when I cook and chop with raw onions, garlic and the like, Lemon Balm is the best natural deodorant. After washing my hands, I "rinse" them in my Lemon Balm plant right outside my kitchen door.

The name "balm" is a contraction of "balsam," and it has entered our language to describe 'that which soothes.' The herb is used for the same healing today as it was in Grecian times.

Botanical Name

Lemon Balm — _Melissa officinalis_ — is known as Balm, Lemon Balm, Sweet Balm, or Sweet Melissa; but it should not be confused with Bee Balm, *Monarda didyma*.

Variegated Balm — _Melissa officinalis_ 'Variegata' ('Aurea') — is a variety of balm with mixed yellow and green leaves that is particularly attractive.

Golden Lemon Balm — _Melissa officinalis_ 'All Gold' — is an all yellow leaved form that turns toward green in the summer.

The name *Melissa* is the Greek word for bee, and bees truly love this plant, especially when it's blooming in July and August. Although I grow many butterfly and bee attracting plants in my half acre garden, the favorite for both is the Lemon Balm. Isn't that reason enough to grow at least one in your garden or planter?

Balm is a member of the mint family, _Labiatae_. It looks and grows much like mint although it doesn't send out as many runners. I find it quite easy to control in its confined location.

History

Balm symbolizes 'pleasantry' and 'longevity,' and has the scent of lemon *and* honey. It has been popular among herbalists for more than 2,000 years. Lemon Balm was used by the Roman naturalist, Pliny, to stop bleeding and by the ancient Greek physician, Dioscorides, for relief of pain in skin wounds. Some felt that balm causes the mind and heart to become merry.

The Arabs were very fond of the balm plant as they believed it was good for heart disorders as well as for lifting the spirits. Arab doctors, during the tenth century, recommended balm to be drunk as a tea for nervousness and anxiety. Adding this herb to wine to treat a variety of illnesses was very common. Balm wine or tea was recommended to scholars for sharp memories and clearheadedness, but also recommended to insomniacs for its sleep-inducing properties. Quite a contradiction, but I guess it worked for them like a small dose of Valium.

Lemon Balm originally came from Southern Europe but is now naturalized in Europe and North Africa as well. It currently grows wild and is cultivated throughout much of the world including many parts of the United States.

Although balm also lifted the spirits of the North American colonists, they had surprisingly few uses for this herb. Thomas Jefferson grew Lemon Balm at Monticello, and its branches were used as a 'strewing herb,' laid on the floor to freshen the room. Early settlers used balm mainly to treat cramps and induce sweating, an old remedy for fever. Nineteenth century physicians considered balm a 'moderate' stimulant when compared to the many other choices of herbs that were available.

 ## TYPE: Perennial *(hardy)*

Lemon Balm is quite hardy in our area, withstanding temperatures to below 10° F. I have not had to replace my plant in over eight years even though we have had some pretty severe winter conditions. Being herbaceous, the above-ground leaves and stems die back each winter, but the root is perennial. On a year-by-year basis, the Lemon Balm is probably one of the most dependable herbs to reappear each spring, right along with the robins. In fact, it is usually the first herb I see leafing out above ground on cold March days.

Description

This mint-like, fast-spreading perennial grows two to three feet tall, and equally wide. The two-foot long stems are somewhat sprawling, but the plants are not invasive like their notorious mint cousins. The stems are characteristically square like other members in the mint family. Unlike mint, which rapidly spreads by underground rhizomes, Lemon Balm forms a clump that can become quite large. If you overindulge in a Lemon Balm frenzy and plant too many, you may be surprised how hard they can be to get rid of because of their dense, penetrating root network. This herb has a very tenacious character.

Balm is grown for its multipurpose, lemon-scented leaves which are one to three inches long. These leaves are fine, oval-shaped and crinkly green with evenly scalloped edges...they look like they have been clipped with pinking shears. Although the shape is similar don't mistake them for nettles!

From early summer into fall the plant produces small clusters of inconspicuous creamy-white flowers that peep from under the leaves. These flowers are rich in nectar and bloom in bunches...all the better for the bees to find them. Bees, in addition to loving the nectar in this herb, use the Lemon Balm to get their bearings and find the hive again. Exactly how the plant is used by the bees is unknown, but the strong aroma in the breeze aids their direction. The plant also has fruit in smooth little nutlets.

Few herbs are as sweetly cordial — the scent is citrusy but not sharp. (See my recipe for Lemon Balm Cordial in the Recipe section.) It has been described as a musky lemon fragrance and you can enjoy a burst of this lemon fragrance by rubbing the leaves vigorously between your palms and inhaling.

Although many people think this plant is homely, beauty is in the eye of the beholder. I really love its flowing branches and the regal look it gives to the herb garden. A variegated form is available to add a little pizzazz to your foliage scheme. In any case, its usefulness far outweighs any perceived lack of beauty.

Planting & Care Requirements

If you choose to grow this herb from seed it should be sown indoors eight to ten weeks before the expected date of the last frost because the seeds germinate slowly. Do not transplant outdoors until all danger of frost is past as new seedlings are tender. A better way to grow from seed is to sow seeds outdoors in late fall to germinate the following spring. Do not cover the seeds with soil, however, as they are very tiny and germinate well without a soil cover. Keep the seeds moist, and then thin or transplant when they have grown to about two inches tall. Place these transplants about 18 inches apart to allow for some expansion of the maturing plants. If the white flower heads are left on the plant it will gladly self-seed.

Additional plants can also be started from root divisions in early spring when the new leaves first appear, or from stem cuttings taken in spring or summer. Lemon Balm is an early spring riser and you can plant well-rooted specimens outside as soon as the soil can be worked.

Lemon Balm likes sun or partial shade and a light, well-drained, moist soil. Fortunately, this herbaceous plant is quite adaptive, and will do well with less than ideal conditions. Occasional light feedings of fish emulsion and some compost are helpful, but over-fertilization will produce large leaves with little fragrance. This herb prefers a soil with a pH 6.0 to 8.0. Like other lemon-scented herbs and lavender (Chapter 3), Lemon Balm produces more intense flavor and aroma under infertile growing conditions.

This plant is more drought resistant than others of the mint family, thereby requiring less water. Although a Lemon Balm plant will continue to grow in poor conditions, it will produce small and often yellowed leaves, which are not as fragrant, attractive or tasty.

This perennial with pebbly, slightly hairy leaves is easy to grow in sun or shade once it is established. Because of its need for cold weather for dormancy and to complete its annual growth cycle, it does not grow very well in southern or very warm and humid climates. I feel we are very fortunate in our part of the country to have this wonderful herb growing so voluminously with so little care.

If the plants get scruffy-looking, they can be kept compact by cutting the stalks back by half after the small, white flowers have faded. Pruning helps regain its more compact shape as well. I like to cut some branches and strew them on the lawn just before my husband, Charles, mows so he can enjoy the refreshing fragrance as well. The mown Lemon Balm along with the grass clippings also gives our compost pile a much needed improved aroma!

Lemon Balm planted near a variety of scented geraniums makes a wonderful companion and a real 'nose' treat each time you enter the garden. Balm can also be planted along a path where you may brush against them, releasing their lemony freshness into the air. This scent seems to permeate the air and remain aloft for some time.

This herb can also be grown indoors but requires at least five hours of direct sunlight a day. Indoors, the plant should be pruned periodically to produce a bushy plant just six to eight inches high. Leaves on an indoor plant can be picked when the plant reaches a height of six inches.

Powdery mildew can be a problem with a damp, sunless condition. I have never had this happen, but if it occurs and much of the plant is affected, the whole plant should be removed from the garden so the mildew condition does not spread. During hot and humid summers, spider mites may become a problem but can be treated with insecticidal soap (such as Safer brand). If aphids become a problem you can bring in the ladybugs or lacewings! They will eat hundreds of aphids for you — nature's way.

During times of high heat stress — not often in my King County neighborhood — the plant can look pale and peaked with slightly bronze-colored woody stems. If this occurs you can cut the plant back and apply some compost and fish fertilizer to help it regain its original vigor.

Lemon Balm will set seed easily. To avoid establishing it as a weed in your garden, cut it back about mid-summer or later and do not put the plant stems in your compost as every seed can germinate! The plant will continue to grow from the base with fresh new growth.

All of this sounds much more complicated than it really is. In eight years of tending my one and only Lemon Balm, it has never had bugs, disease or heatstroke. It just blooms along willingly and keeps producing its lovely aroma season after season and attracting the bees, the butterflies, and the children. A true herbal beginner's plant. So easy to grow and so much to enjoy!

 Harvesting

In Lemon Balm's first year it may appear too scrawny to spare many leaves. That's a normal condition, but in the second year you will be rewarded with an ample harvest! Fresh leaves of Lemon Balm can be picked for use at any time. Simply pinch a branch back to a set of leaves. You can obtain up to three full harvests in one season by cutting off the entire plant above ground level. Generally, only the leaves are harvested and used, but the small white flowers can be picked and scattered in salads as well. A mature plant produces two cups of fresh leaves when it is first harvested, and two slightly less bountiful harvests later in the season. When measuring herbs by the cup, press them down rather than packing them loosely. Be careful not to bruise the foliage when you harvest as this will dissipate much of the fragrance and flavor.

When I am fortunate to have an abundant harvest in mid-summer, I like to pick a bunch of stems with the leaves attached, soak them in water, and place on my barbecue while grilling fish or poultry. It not only adds a wonderful flavor to the entreé but seems to wake up my neighborhood as well. What's for dinner, Carol?

Preservation

Although Lemon Balm in dried form loses some of its intense flavor that makes it so endearing in the summer months, it is still worth your time to dry some for the winter months.

To harvest leaves for drying, cut just before or after flowering. Just before the balm plant blooms, its oils are heavily concentrated. Cut about one quarter off the top of the plant and rinse any dirt from the leaves. Because the leaves strip so easily from the fresh plant, I accomplish this before drying. Lay these leaves one layer deep and separated so they do not overlap on the drying trays. If you are drying a large harvest, you may want to try piling them several inches deep in the trays but leaving them on the stems. With this method, you can remove the dried leaves from the stems after they are thoroughly dry. Air will circulate nicely around the mounded branches. With the heat set at about 90-110° F. in the dehydrator, dry until the leaves are crisp but not crumbly. To retain color and flavor, dry as quickly as possible, as the leaves will turn black if dried too slowly. Any discolored leaves should be discarded. You can also dry Lemon Balm in the shade outdoors by spreading on trays or screens if there is no moisture in the air and good circulation around the leaves. To keep the leaves clean, cover the trays or screens with cheesecloth.

If you are not bringing the plant indoors at the end of the growing season, you may harvest to ground level for preserving all of the remaining leaves.

After drying, store the whole leaves in containers that will keep them dry, free of mold and at their flavorful best. You can use glass spice jars, vitamin bottles, screw top jelly jars, (or for larger amounts, canning jars, flour or coffee canisters) as long as they have tight-fitting lids. I like to use transparent containers so I can see the supply I have left, and it also makes it easy to check to see if moisture is condensing inside. This is critical during the first week or so. If you see a mist or droplets forming inside the glass, you will know that the leaves still have some moisture in them and will soon become moldy or rot. Promptly pour them out and dry them for another few hours or briefly in an oven turned at the lowest temperature. I usually label and date my jars or packages because once the herbs are dried it's surprisingly difficult to tell some of them apart.

Lemon Balm will keep satisfactorily for several years although it may lose some of its flavor after a year. Dried balm leaves can also be powdered for use, especially for medicinal purposes or as added flavoring to cookies and cakes.

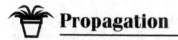 ## Propagation

Lemon Balm can be a slow starter but it is both prolific and hardy once established. Although it grows willingly from seeds, it is better to germinate the seeds overnight by scarifying or soaking in warm water before planting.

I prefer to start Lemon Balm from root divisions or stem cuttings instead of from seeds. (See Lavender, Chapter 3 for these propagating instructions.) To divide the roots in early spring, simply dig up the entire plant, separate into portions and replant about 36 inches apart in separate spots in your garden. This is a great way to start a wonderfully fragrant hedge at almost no cost.

An even better way to start Lemon Balm is to get a seedling from a friend. I have given away many little six-inch plants — especially to children in the neighborhood. Even small children can very successfully grow this herb and they love sniffing it daily in their garden and learn quickly to sprinkle it on fruit, etc. It's easy to start these new plants by taking a small stem with roots attached when it first comes up in the spring. I put these seedlings in potting soil with a small amount of diluted 20-20-20 fertilizer.

Once established, a mature Lemon Balm readily reseeds itself, which is an advantage if you want to give away lots of these little, lemony herbs to the neighborhood children.

If you have too many seeds of Lemon Balm developing, you might invite a flock of black-capped chickadees to your garden and they will gladly attack the stalks with great ferocity and determination in search of this favorite seed. Actually, I find several birds love the seeds of this herb as well as many of my other ones. A true bird paradise. Because of this bird sanctuary around the Lemon Balm plant, I never have too many seedlings spring up unwanted as others complain about.

╫╿╽ Culinary Uses

Lemon Balm is usually used raw, seldom in cooked dishes, but adds a subtly sweet flavor to a variety of foods however it is prepared. If used in cooked dishes, add the balm very near the end of the cooking time or its oils will dissipate completely with the heat. In baked goods and breads, however, the lemon flavor holds up well as it's captured in the surrounding dough. This delicate, flavorful herb is generally used with light foods; green salads, fruit salads, veal, poultry, or fish, shellfish and lamb. Lemon Balm is also a favorite herb, along with mint, to garnish summer drinks. When preparing the leaves, be sure to tear them with your fingers, because using a knife will discolor them and add a metallic taste to the delicate flavor.

Lemon Balm is a perfect tea herb because almost everyone loves the flavor. It mixes very well with other tea herbs. Try it with raspberry or strawberry leaves, rose hips, alfalfa, mints, red clover, or scented basils. Try several combinations. My favorite combination is Lemon Balm, Lemon Verbena, mints, and/or scented geranium leaves. The mild, yet lemony, flavor can be achieved for steaming hot mugs or tall glasses of naturally sweet, lemon-scented iced tea by steeping a small handful of fresh leaves in a pot of freshly boiled water for eight minutes. This can be served hot or cold over ice. A strong Lemon Balm tea can be used to stew fruit (reconstituted dried fruit or fresh).

Use balm alone, in blends, or in fruit punch. Little sprigs of balm make pretty, edible garnishes for gelatin, sherbet, *sorbet,* and ice cream as well as for fruit drinks and teas.

Fresh leaves will add a mild citrus tang to green salads and its flavor blends well with other herbs. Like any herb or flower in a tossed salad, use sparingly as each flavor can sometimes overwhelm the careful taste subtleties you have created. When using herbs in a salad, I use no more than one eighth of the salad as herbal ingredients. One half cup of fresh herbs to seven or eight cups of greens and edible flowers makes a large, beautiful salad.

Use the balm leaves generously, however, in sauces and stuffing, and for chicken and fish. I have given you a favorite chicken recipe below that I use every summer on the outdoor barbecue grill. For baking or roasting indoors, you can cover a whole chicken with balm leaves after placing it in your cooking pot.

For a simple fruit drink or wine cup, bruise a few leaves and put in a glass of fruit juice or white wine for an uplifting drink. Try placing a sprig in each jar of homemade rhubarb jam. Several shredded teaspoons of balm give a nice flavor to creamed soups and salad dressings as well. Try safflower or canola oil for a superb dressing.

My favorite vegetables with Lemon Balm are corn, broccoli, asparagus and green beans. The herb should be added at the end of the cooking time or sprinkled on the vegetables when served. Instead of salt on the vegetables, try lemon pepper along with the Lemon Balm.

To use Lemon Balm fresh, recipes aren't really necessary as it is so easy. You will note that I have given you just five ideas for recipes and uses in a following section.

In my garden, Lemon Balm is one of three herbs that I use for sweetening. The others are mint(s) and Sweet Cicely. Because the Lemon Balm is such a prolific producer, I always have some, fresh or dried, for use in desserts or cool drinks, and to perk up vegetables year around.

Medicinal Uses

As noted earlier in the history section, balm has been used for many years in a variety of healing lotions, potions, compresses and infusions. For such an unpretentious plant, it has an impressive medicinal record.

Stress-related headaches, tiredness, nausea, tension, sore throat, toothache, insomnia, arthritis, bronchitis, asthma, viral cold sores and herpes, digestive problems, nervous stomach, and menstrual cramps have all had Lemon Balm prescribed successfully — so many ailments, in fact, that balm became known as a cure-all.

Recent research indicates that a hot water extract of Lemon Balm may have strong antiviral properties. It appears that Lemon Balm can have a positive effect on all of these mentioned maladies. And to think I drink the tea just because it tastes good!

Charlemagne ordered this herb grown in all the physic gardens because it was popular as a tranquilizer and sedative. It is said that, 'Lemon Balm causes the mind and heart to become merry and drive away all troubles.' It sure works for me, and I know it will for you, too.

I think we have found the cure to discontent, anger, miscommunication, and downright ornery dispositions. If we could just market this precious commodity throughout the world under a fancy name, we would have a real solution to many of our world's ills!

❓ Other Uses

Lemon Balm is a particularly good herb for use in cosmetic lotions. A steamy Lemon Balm facial is good for acne, and as a lotion cleanser it will help prevent wrinkles. For hair care, it can be used as a wonderful rinse for blondes when steeped as "tea," allowed to cool, and used after shampoo. This leaves blonde hair with a shine and fragrant lemon essence.

Cosmetic vinegars made with Lemon Balm are used as skin toners. For a relaxing bath, tie a handful of balm in a cloth and run your bath water over it. You will feel its calming effect as well as enjoy the splendid, lemony fragrance. Sachets, *potpourris*, herb/sleep cushions, and fresh bouquets are all good uses for this bounteous and redolent herb.

I recently read in *The Herb Companion* magazine of a gentleman who uses Lemon Balm along with sage, strawberry leaves, and thyme to create a 'gentlemen's bath *pourri*'. He says it works for him, and I'm sure other gentlemen would agree if they tried it.

When you are out of lemon-scented furniture polish, try rubbing balm leaves into the wood. The plant's oils work like the oily polishes and the furniture will take on a lemony smell and shine.

Here's a unique way to use the extra stems and leaves of this voluminous herb. Stuff a handful in each 'used' sneaker — yours or your children's — to aerate, deodorize, and freshen them! The closets will definitely smell better.

This plant will also repel certain insects. Rub down a picnic table before dining to keep the ants away or toss leaves into a campfire to deter the mosquitoes and other flying insects.

Like most herbs, I have found so many uses for Lemon Balm besides in culinary dishes, that I am sure I would grow it in my garden for these uses alone. But I do love the tea!

Recipes

Lemon Balm Cordial

In an electric blender, measure one quarter cup fresh **ginger root,** coarsely chopped, one and one half teaspoons whole **cloves,** one two-inch stick of **cinnamon,** two tablespoons **lavender blossoms or buds,** one tablespoon each of **coriander seed, fennel seed, fresh rosemary, fresh sage,** and **fresh thyme,** one quarter cup fresh **Lemon Balm leaves** and tender stems, one quarter cup fresh **Cinnamon Basil,** four **bay leaves,** broken, with one cup water. Blend this mixture to a coarse consistency. Combine mixture with two liters of **brandy or vodka** and put in a two-quart glass container. Store in a cool, dark place for at least one month, shaking occasionally. Strain the liquid into a clean bottle, cork or seal tightly and store in a cool, dark place. Use in small quantities with meats, poultry, sauces, and soups. A few drops in boiling water will produce a soothing herbal tea.

Now I know this isn't a recipe you would try every day, but I wanted to include just one cordial-type recipe for those of you who might really want to be adventurous and try something exotic!

Easy-to-make Punch

Bring one third cup **sugar** and two thirds cup **water** to boil and set aside. Add one quarter cup each of freshly squeezed **lemon juice, orange juice, chopped mint, and Lemon Balm leaves.** Cover and steep for an hour. Strain the mixture and add two quarts of **ginger ale.** Serve sparkling and chilled.

You may also use **diet ginger ale** or **iced tea** for the liquid. This is really a great thirst quencher during hot, dusty weather.

Lemon Balm Garnish

Use a couple of handfuls of fresh picked, and coarsely torn, **Lemon Balm leaves** and place in two ice cube trays, distributing evenly on the bottom of each. Place a small piece or two of

fresh fruit in each cup, like sliced **strawberry, orange, lemon or lime wedge** (peeled,) or a whole **raspberry,** on top of the leaves. Lastly, layer an **edible flower blossom** in each cube; scented geranium, rose petals, pansies, or borage are all beautiful. Fill trays carefully with water and freeze. Use the cubes in glasses of iced tea, lemonade, or sparkling water summer drinks.

One caution if you are using flowers, be sure they have not been sprayed with insecticide or herbicides. I keep one small area of my garden with edible flowers that are never sprayed, except with Safer Soap, so they can be used in drinks and other culinary recipes. Edible flowers with herbs are a fun and easy way to create some spectacular dishes.

Chicken Breast With Lemon Balm

For two chicken breasts (bone in), tear coarsely one handful (one half cup) of **Lemon Balm leaves.** Mix in some finely chopped **green onions or fresh chopped chives** and place under the skin of the chicken. Sprinkle the outer chicken lightly with **lemon pepper** and grill over medium heat. You may want to baste moderately with a little melted butter during grilling, but watch for any flare-ups. Grill until no longer pink in the center.

This is an exception to using Lemon Balm uncooked, but the mild lemon flavor imparts a nice aroma and subtle flavor to the chicken. You can, of course, eat the Lemon Balm leaves along with the chicken, or remove them and/or the skin before serving.

A second way to use Lemon Balm with chicken is to cover a whole roasting chicken with leaves. Place on a rack in a covered roasting pan. Roast at 325° F. until the inside temperature reaches 185° F. Let the poultry set a few minutes before carving. Pour off juices and remove the fat that has accumulated. Add a little white wine to the defatted broth in the roasting pan and cook to thicken. Drizzle over sliced roast chicken.

This chicken recipe works with a number of different culinary herbs and has always been a crowd pleaser at my table — and so simple.

Cantaloupe Sorbet With Lemon Balm

Dissolve one quarter cup of **sugar** in one cup of **boiling water** along with 10-12 **Lemon Balm leaves.** Bring the syrup to a simmer and cook for a few minutes. Remove from the heat and let cool to room temperature. Remove the seeds from one **cantaloupe** and cut pulp into chunks (there should be three and one half to four cups). Remove the herb leaves from the syrup. In a food processor or blender, puree the melon with the syrup in batches until smooth. Pour the puree into an ice cream maker and stir in one cup chilled *Asti Spumante.* Freeze in an ice cream maker according to instructions. Without an ice cream maker, you can freeze in a tray. Remove from freezer after a couple of hours and stir to aerate. Refreeze and restir a couple of times. I have found this method quite satisfactory. Be sure the *sorbet* is quite firmly frozen before serving. Garnish scoops with **Lemon Balm leaves.**

 Other Notes

Lemon Balm is, perhaps, the very best herb for children to grow. It is pretty much fail-safe and produces so well; the child really can feel a sense of accomplishment with his or her very first try.

As an ornamental outside of the herb garden, it is best to use a variegated leaf variety as it is more attractive, especially as a border plant. You might like a hedge with alternating green and variegated Lemon Balms. Because these are in leaf for most of the year, they make a splendid border. As the season progresses, however, these will look less and less different as the variegation lessens as the summer moves along.

Remember, Lemon Balm is also especially fine for attracting butterflies as well as bees. In the summer time I have counted as many as 50 bees at one time on my plant with a variety of butterflies fluttering around it at the same time. This is reason enough to grow Lemon Balm even if it wasn't such a 'cure-all' and so tasty.

Mint

*The One You Can't
Live Without*

Mint

M int has more virtues than money, or so I have read. Therefore, it symbolizes virtue. In the language of herbs, it also stands for cheerfulness and wisdom.

Every herb garden must have mint or mints — at least one! The species *Mentha* is a whole story in itself, with members that have intriguing flavors like apples, oranges and grapefruit, to lemon, pineapple and ginger. Because mints are ready growers, even a lazy gardener can keep several varieties. Among these: Spearmint, for use in teas and with meats and vegetables; Applemint, a mild, sweet mint that's good in fruit dishes; Peppermint, for jellies, sauces, sweets and ices; Pineapple Mint and Orange Mint, citrusy varieties for iced drinks. My recommendation is to grow any or all of these. There really is a mint to please every palate and complement nearly every food.

Many of our modern medicines are chemical substitutes for plant extracts, especially from herbs such as mint. I have included several suggestions for using this fragrant herb in healthful ways as well as in culinary dishes.

Last year I grew Apple, Orange, and Curly Mint, but I have tried 12-15 different mint varieties over the years. Which is my favorite? All of them, of course! All mints are easy to grow and fun to use. They are like special friends that come to visit each spring and welcome me with their fragrantly delightful gifts.

Botanical Name

Profusion, infusion, and confusion characterize the mint species, *Mentha* . . . profusion because of its growing habits and many members; infusion because of its long history as a medicinal and social tea; and confusion because of its large number of varieties.

There are at least 25 main species of mint and hundreds of hybrids, variants and cultivars. All the mints were considered one plant — mint — until 1696, when British botanist John Ray differentiated them using the binomial nomenclature system. Many of the plants in the *Mentha* species are named for their scent much as basils are named.

I have given you botanical information on a number of mints below because they are so individual in flavor and aroma.

Mentha are all members of the *Labiatae* family.

Water Mint — *Mentha aquatica* — is heart-shaped and has a very strong scent, somewhat hay-like, that is not as pleasant as other mints.

Bergamot Mint — *M. x piperita* var. *citrata* — is also known as *'Eau de Cologne'* or Orange Mint, and is more aromatic than Aquatica Mint. It is naturalized in most of North America, and has a very strong citrus fragrance and flavor. It is very soothing in herbal teas and makes an excellent *potpourri* as well. This very unusual mint is extremely vigorous.

Curlimint — *M. aquatica* var. *citrata* — has small, curled light green leaves with a crisp mint flavor that grows along stream beds. This decorative variety is sometimes used as a garnish but goes well in iced tea and juleps.

Peppermint — *M. x piperita* — does have a hint of pepper taste and is the liveliest member of the mint family. It's fragrant, flavorful and beautiful with reddish-black stems, and has small, smooth, slightly pointed dark green leaves, and pale purple flowers. This is a sterile hybrid of *M. aquatica* and *M. spicata*. Peppermint is healthful and discourages insects. This variety is prized by expert herbalists and novice gardeners alike.

Blue Balsam — *M. x piperita* 'Mitcham' — is recognizable with its deep purple-blue cast of stems and leaves. For a tea of dried mint, the 'Blue Balsam' in this peppermint species is superb because it does have a slightly sweet, balsamic taste. The flavor and smell of the leaves seem to intensify and improve with drying. Other variants in this 'Mitcham' subspecies are 'Candymint', 'Chocolate', and 'Blackstem', all potent but so marvelous, but confused in the trade.

Spearmint — *M. spicata* — is most commonly used in the kitchen in an uncooked state. It is a popular upright and vigorous grower with bright hairless, pointed leaves and long spikes of lilac flowers. The leaves provide a flavoring for meats, particularly lamb, and herbal mint jelly. This is the best mint for a window box and has a milder flavor than peppermint.

Applemint — *M. suaveolens* — is my favorite for tea. It is also sometimes referred to as Woolly Mint or Egyptian Mint, and has been catalogued as *Mentha x villosa alopecuroides*. It has hairy stems and grayish-green leaves. This species has spikes of pale lilac and is the tallest of the mints, sometimes growing to a height of three feet. It tastes of ripe apple and spearmint with a fruity scent. The leaves are very nice when candied. Applemint is less prone to rust disease than other mints.

Pineapple Mint — *M. suaveolens* 'Variegata' — has small, light green leaves with white edges. This has a mildly sweet and fruity pineapple flavor and is very decorative. The Pineapple Mint usually grows just one foot tall. The suaveolens varieties are easy to recognize because of their fuzzy leaves, and they all have a fruity aroma.

English Pennyroyal — *M. pulegium* — is a low, creeping mint with a heady, pungent aroma and a strong taste. Its prostrate growing habit is an exception to other mints which are upright. This mint likes the shade and will help repel fleas. The flowers are in dense clusters at leaf axils and make a good ground cover; it's a little easier to grow than Corsican Mint for that purpose. This variety is winter hardy only to 5 F°. Pennyroyal is generally used in flea collars and in *potpourri*.

Corsican Mint — *M. requienii* — is bright green with leaves just 3/8 inches long. It, too, has a prostrate growth. This mint is especially used around stepping stones because it gives off such a magnificently strong scent when crushed. It likes all nooks and crevices and will reseed itself under the right conditions. Although used in this way, Corsican Mint will not survive with a great deal of traffic walking over it. This mint can be tricky because it needs the right combination of fast-draining soil and frequent watering. *Cremé de Menthe* liqueur has this distinctive flavor.

Yerba Buena — *M. cordifolia* — is an essential flavoring in Latin American dishes. The flavor is similar to spearmint but a bit coarser. In Mexico, they call *yerba buena*, the good herb.

History

Most mints are native to the Old World. Many are now naturalized throughout North America from Southern Canada to Mexico.

Mints that grew in Egypt spread to Palestine, where history records that the Pharisees of Biblical times paid their tithes with mint. In Luke 11:42, Jesus scolds the Pharisees: "You pay tithes of mint and rue...but neglect justice and the love of God." Quite an admonishment. From the Holy Land mint spread to Greece and entered Greek mythology as a symbol of hospitality.

The Greeks used mint in various herbal treatments and temple rites. They believed it could clear the voice, cure hiccups, and counteract sea serpent stings. (I wonder if those are the same as jellyfish?) It was also used in their athletic ceremonies and strewn around their kitchens and sick rooms as it symbolized strength.

The Romans crowned themselves with Peppermint wreaths and adorned their halls with it in preparation for feasts so that the smell would stimulate the guests.

A garland of Pennyroyal leaves was worn to treat headache in Medieval Europe. In England in the nineteenth century, mint was strewn on the floors of modest dwellings and public buildings as well, in the belief that the scent prevented the spread of disease.

Peppermint and Spearmint came to the 'New World' with the colonists, who also used them medicinally. They found the Native Indians were already using indigenous American mints to treat coughs, chest congestion and pneumonia. The colonists, however, introduced Spearmint and Peppermint, and the plants quickly went wild. They drank mint tea for headaches, heartburn, indigestion, gas, and to help them sleep. They also drank mint tea for pure pleasure — especially since it wasn't taxed by England — but also simply because it tasted good...and it still does!

Mint Juleps were created in the 1800's shortly after the birth of Kentucky Straight Bourbon. Several recipes were developed for making it, and many stories were told of it. One thing was certain, a man shouldn't take his Mint Julep lightly — the Mint Julep was a sophisticated drink for a refined gentleman. A 19th century Southern gentleman noted that creating a Mint Julep is a rite that must not be entrusted to a novice, a statistician, or a Yankee.

Commercial cultivation of Peppermint and Spearmint dates from 1750 in England and by 1790 the industry had migrated to the United States. Here in the Pacific Northwest mints grow well in our fertile, sandy-loam soils.

Japanese Mint is the primary source of menthol and is cultivated in Japan, Taiwan, the People's Republic of China, Paraguay, Brazil, Argentina, and India. Peppermint oil is produced by the White Mint, a small plant that grows around Mitchum, England. In Mexico they call mint, *yerba buena,* the good herb!

TYPE: Perennial *(hardy)*

Most mints are considered perennial plants and are quite hardy to -20° F., but they should be replaced every three years or so for best flavor production. This herb grows throughout the world from moist, shady spots to deserts. Pennyroyal and Corsican Mint are sometimes treated as annuals in our climate as they do not stand up well in wet, cold winters.

 # Description

Generally speaking, mint leaves may be rounded, oval, or slightly pointed; smooth or wrinkly; and have slightly toothed or serrated edges. The most distinctive features of the mints is their square-shaped stems. Depending on the variety, mints grow from just two inches to more than three feet tall.

Most species are invasive perennials, which send up new plants from their spreading roots. Since mints interbreed readily, it can be difficult to determine the exact species. They grow to a height of one to three feet depending on the variety and the growing conditions. The tiny flowers are purple, pink or white; and in whorls in terminal spikes and they flower in July and August. The leaves are opposite on the stems and are simple, toothed, and very fragrant. The fruit is small nutlets. All mints have characteristically aromatic foliage and flowers which are highly cultivated for their oil and flavoring.

Planting & Care Requirements

Every gardener wants at least one mint plant in his/her herb garden. If you have a landscape you prefer to be semi-wild, mint is a good choice since it will grow unchecked as ground cover. You can have a lovely thick carpet outdoors by letting the tougher mints (Peppermint, Applemint, Spearmint) grow. Just mow them as they come into flower and they will reward you with an aromatic landscape.

Mints prefer light, rich, well-drained and loamy soil that is kept *frequently* and *consistently* damp. Soil pH 6.5 is ideal, however, mints have been grown in poorer soils as well. Mints like the sun but they will accept some shade like another member of this family, Lemon Balm. Some actually grow better when they receive some shade each day.

Like most herbs, mint doesn't need fertilizer unless you want to give it a small amount of fish emulsion. If your soil is quite acid, add dolomite limestone and bone meal to counteract the acidity. The plants like compost mulch in summer and winter as they are prolific growers and use up the nutrients fairly quickly.

Don't dress the topsoil around the plants with fresh manure or add too much organic matter, as this will only encourage water retention and rust, a fungal disease. Too much watering will particularly encourage the rust problem. Rust can be identified by light-yellow, blister-like lesions on young shoots in spring or brownish-red spots surrounded by a yellow halo on the leaves. If rust invades the plant, turning most of the leaves a brown color, the diseased plants should be dug up and burned. Don't put them in a compost pile. For minor rust problems, the roots of the mint should be washed in warm water at 110° F. for twenty minutes. The washing alone may remove the rust spores, and thoroughly washed material usually grows free from rust the following year. A complete clean up in the fall can help prevent this fungal disease.

Despite a reputation as a disease free plant, mints are susceptible to certain insects and diseases besides the rust mentioned above. Verticillium wilt is a soil-borne fungus that attacks tomatoes and other summer plants. This wilt will stunt a mint's growth and turn leaves yellow. There is no real cure once it has invaded. Mint anthracnose can be another problem. The pests that might bother your mints include: spider mites, loopers, mint flea beetles, mint root borers, grasshoppers, cutworms, root weevils, and aphids. Before recommending a solution to the problem, you will need to know for sure what is affecting your mint — insect or disease — and specifically which one. An insecticidal soap can be very helpful in the critter instances. I have never had a problem, but if your plants don't look well and you can't determine the cause, you might want to visit your local Master Gardener Clinic with a sample for diagnosis and suggested treatment. In the late fall, after your final harvest, cut the plants back to the ground. This eliminates over-wintering sites for mint pests.

The flea beetle eats small, round holes in the leaves beginning in July. Their eggs are laid in the soil. Strong measures with Malathion may be necessary if a simpler measure of catnip tea does not solve the problem. Spider mites are another familiar pest to mint as they are to other herb plants. Mints do not deter cabbage loopers, although that is a common belief. The larvae of these moths eat large holes in the leaves of both Spearmint and Peppermint. This usually begins around June 20. A biological control is needed for these pests.

Mint's reputation as a vigorous, spreading plant should not be underrated. Like an unruly child, it needs sharp discipline from time to time, depending on the inclination of the gardener. Since mint spreads by underground runners, it should be planted in a container or enclosed area to isolate it from other plants. A variety of devices have been used to contain the spreading of mints. A long terra-cotta chimney flue sunk deeply in the earth supplies one of the best measures of control. You can put individual plants in bottomless cans about 18 inches deep or surround them with metal strips 18 inches deep to prevent roots from spreading outward. The roots grow downward about six to eight inches and then horizontally. With barriers at this level the mints will be somewhat contained. However, the roots will wiggle out of pots and other containers, no matter how deep, to eventually find a place in the earth of their own. It's better to be safe with deep root protection than have your mint spread throughout the garden.

Of course, like many new herb gardeners, I didn't do that the first year I planted mint, and guess what? My whole herb bed became mint runners by the second year. I then needed to take up *all* the plants, laboriously separate roots, and rework the soil in the bed before I could replant. Don't let this happen to you. It will create a loathing of mint!

I now grow three mint plants a year in a rectangular wooden planter about three feet long by 10" wide and 12" deep. I use wooden roofing shingles vertically to the bottom of the container to separate the three varieties. With different mints planted near each other, they need to be clipped regularly so that they do not cross pollinate. Frequent cutting will keep mints at their prettiest because it encourages the stems to branch out and makes the plants more lush and healthier.

If winters are quite severe in your area, you might want to mulch with straw or pine needles, especially if the plants are in containers. Most mints will begin to get a little woody and weedy after several years and should be replaced. Container plants can be replaced or take fresh cuttings every two to three years, but less often if they are in the open garden — perhaps every five years or so.

Mints make good indoor plants, but they will respond better if started outdoors and then brought in at the end of the summer season. These indoor plants need to be divided and repotted every year.

Harvesting

Most mint plants may be cut two or three times a year, much like Lemon Balm, leaving a few inches of stem to grow again. An early and mid-summer cutting should be taken two to three inches above the ground. Give the plants a boost at this time with a fish fertilizer emulsion. The late harvest should take place just before flowering or when the lower leaves yellow, whichever comes first. Cut the plants back to the ground at this time.

If you have an entire area with only mint, cut the mint back in the fall, and dig into the bed all over with a sharp spade. Wet the bed down and cover it with top soil or mulch. Next season, the cut runners will propagate richly.

If it becomes necessary to harvest lots of mint to keep the area from being inundated, you can put the leftovers in your compost pile. The mint dies quickly when uprooted and won't take root in your compost — although it will make it smell better!

Preservation

All kinds of mints dry very nicely and keep their individual aromas if picked and dried at their peak. The young tender leaves in the spring can be harvested and preserved as soon as they appear. They have more flavor than the older leaves, which tend to become a little woody. You also can freeze the leaves as described in earlier chapters. I do prefer drying mint leaves instead of freezing, however, because it stores so much easier and the intense flavor remains until I crumble the dried leaves just before use.

Leaves should be stripped from the stems to dry, whether using a dehydrator or an oven. Again, I prefer the dehydrator method for best results. Although some flavor is lost in the oven method, it can be helpful if the humidity is too high to successfully air dry. Spread the leaves on a rack with fiberglass screening in a single layer and dry in an oven at 150° F. for two to three hours with the oven door cracked open to allow moisture to escape. Check them often during this time, however, as some varieties dry much sooner than others.

Mint, because of its long stems, dries very well when hung as described under Lavender (Chapter 3). Remember to save the dried mint stems to use in the fireplace for a winter's evening pleasure. You can also soak the stems for twenty minutes and then place on the barbecue coals before grilling outdoors for a refreshing aroma and wonderful flavor. I sometimes save the dried stems and place in a bath bag to use on a hot day when a tepid, minted bath is a real relaxer.

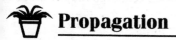 **Propagation**

Don't let someone try to sell you a packet of Peppermint seeds — there is no such thing! Now isn't that a good thing to know? Peppermint is a sterile hybrid and must be propagated by cuttings, division, or layering. In fact this is the best way to propagate all the mints. It's the only way to be sure you get the plant you want as they cross breed so readily with the help of the birds, the bees, and other mints nearby.

The best way to start a mint plant is to get a root division from a friend. Your friends (or enemies, for that matter) will probably be happy to give away some of this plentiful plant! It's much better to buy a plant from a nursery or secure a division from a friend to be sure of the variety.

The mints reproduce by sending long, lateral stolons or runners, under the ground. You can take tip cuttings in summer from those varieties you like the best and the cuttings will root easily in moist potting soil, or even in water. They will be ready to repot for fall. If you wish to divide established plants, do it in the fall or early spring. You need only one rooted stem of each variety or a small clump to produce further plants, as they will increase quite readily. Do you have friends to whom you may give the remainders? I pot up several each spring to donate to plant sales.

My three mints in the wooden container are emptied in early spring. I take one small root from each plant and replant in fresh potting soil and discard the remainder of the plants — or sometimes I pot them in smaller pots to give to my little friends in the neighborhood. These children are getting quite a collection and, fortunately, their parents don't seem to mind.

🍴 Culinary Uses

Mint flavor is assertive and unmistakable, yet it has a wide variety of uses in the kitchen from subtle accents to major flavor statements.

Although Peppermint is the premier choice for flavoring candy, gum, and other sweets, it is a bit strong for other uncooked culinary uses. Peppermint used in cooked foods, especially soup, makes a surprisingly vivid flavor enhancer. Some chopped mint sprinkled into the bottom of a soup bowl with tomato, pea, cucumber or chicken soup ladled on top is particularly satisfying. Try a sprig on top of a cup of hot chocolate.

When using Peppermint for cooking, harvest the young leaves when possible, as the older leaves and stems tend to be more bitter in this plant.

Spearmint enhances all sorts of meat, fish, and vegetable dishes. It mingles well with veal, eggplant, white beans, black beans, lentils, cracked wheat salads, fruit salads and fruit beverages. Mint is perhaps most associated with peas, lamb, jellies, sauces, candy and chocolate. Welsh cooks even add mint to the boiling water when they prepare cabbage. I think I'll try that, it is bound to make the house smell better!

Mint has been popular for centuries in Greek, Arabic, North Africa, Middle Eastern, Sicilian, and Indian foods. It is used to cool the fiery bite of peppers in the popular Thai and Vietnamese dishes.

To use mint flowers, rinse the flower heads to remove any insects, and shake or pat them dry. The flower heads can be used as garnishes, or the individual florets can be stripped from their stems and scattered on salads or soups. They are a bit milder than the leaves and have a delicate minty perfume. I especially like the flowers in green salad in combination with arugula (roquette), and more traditional lettuce varieties.

Try fresh, minced mint leaves combined with plain yogurt and sliced cucumbers or on cottage cheese. Add fresh mint to tuna salad, then dress with a lime vinaigrette. Prepare an herb vinegar using fresh mint and orange zest. The spiced mint vinegar recipe I have given you in a following section is outstanding. Some who smell the finished product want to drink it like a beverage because it smells so good. Use this vinegar as a marinade for lamb and in dressing for spring salads. An easy sauce for lamb or pork can be made by simmering vinegar, sugar and freshly chopped mint for a few minutes. It gives a great tangy sweet and sour, as well as a minty, flavor.

As a dessert idea, try a little **Grand Marnier** drizzled over sliced fresh fruit and sprinkle with finely chopped mint. That's real gourmet eating, and very simple. Other dessert ideas include sprinkling mint on baked apples, using in sherbet or *sorbet*, and flavoring icings and frostings. Fresh peas and carrots can be lightly steamed and then sauteed in butter slightly sweetened with honey, adding a teaspoon of grated orange zest and a few tablespoons of chopped mint. Mint in condiments is often used as a palate cleanser to spicy food.

Dried leaves are best used in teas and dishes that are hot, because the fragrance and taste do not stand out in the cooler dishes. A favorite tea combination is mint with Lemon Balm and Sweet Cicely, but this also makes a great combination for salad dressings.

If you wish to experiment in combining mint with other fresh herbs, try basil, cress, dill, Lemon Balm, parsley and/or tarragon.

In many cultures, mint is more than just an occasional seasoning. In the Middle East, it plays a big part in mixed green salads that are unrivaled for their zesty, refreshing flavor.

A rejuvenating mint water can be made by twisting or bruising a cup of Peppermint, Spearmint, or other mint leaves and placing in a clean half gallon container. Fill with fresh, cool water and chill in refrigerator. Strain and serve over ice.

Medicinal Uses

Mint was mentioned as a stomach soother in the Ebers Papyrus, the world's oldest surviving medical text, and it is still used for that purpose today.

It became important as a medicinal herb in the beginning of the 18th century. Various species were used as a cure for colic, digestive odors, and a host of other problems. Japanese Mint was thought to have antifertility properties. Peppermint, in particular, has been said to be the number one herb to take with you if you are stranded for a year on an island. Of course, I don't know how you know ahead you're going to be stranded, but just in case, remember Peppermint. This is the source of the commercially and medicinally important menthol.

Spearmint, which does not contain menthol, is used only for flavor. However, you can wash rough skin and chapped hands with Spearmint tea, gargle with the tea for a sore throat or lay crushed mint leaves on insect bites. It has been used for centuries as a local analgesic for sprains, bruises, and toothache (the Elizabethans also used mint to whiten their teeth). As a massage lotion, crush mint into vegetable oil and steep for several days, then strain and keep on hand for backache massage. To induce sweating with feverish colds, mint and sage may be steeped together in hot water and used as a compress.

Probably the most common use of mint as a hot tea is for indigestion and upset stomach, especially after a meal of rich food or Chinese dishes, as it's helpful for flatulence and relief of muscle spasms. That is the reason mints are historically served after dinner, and as a digestive aid they are frequently a component of today's antacids. By inhaling the steam from mint tea, nasal, sinus, and chest congestion can be relieved. Mint tea is good as a pick-me-up, but also as a hunger depressant...for only a while, however, it isn't a diet remedy. Nothing that tastes that good could be an efficient diet remedy.

As an anesthetic it is used in many pain-relieving skin creams we see on the market today. It also tends to be germicidal in test tube research against several bacteria including herpes. A few drops of Peppermint Oil can be applied directly to affected areas of wounds, burns, and scalds. Researchers in Russia have discovered that Spearmint contains its highest essential oil content when three-fourths of blossoms on its flower spike are open.

Mint really works as a home remedy. And because it tastes good, you don't need a spoonful of sugar to help the medicine go down. This wonderful 'medicinal' herb is non-toxic and perfectly safe to use in home medicines and is included in the Food and Drug Administration's list of herbs generally regarded as safe, except in the case of pregnant women. The strength of the flavor sometimes is not pleasant to young children but they usually prefer the minty taste to other cod liver oil type remedies.

 **Other Uses**

For decorative uses, mint in very popular in herb/sleep pillows, bath bags, *potpourris* and sachets. (The only difference between a *potpourri* and a sachet is the consistency of the ingredients. Sachets have all the flowers crushed to a fine powder and the added spices and citrus peels are finely ground. *Potpourris* are made from coarsely broken herbs, spices, and flowers.) I have listed below a good 'recipe' for a sleep potion for a mint sachet.

For cosmetic uses, fresh mint leaves can be put into the blender with ice cubes on a hot summer day to produce a refreshing, stimulating skin tonic. One of my favorite 'recipes' for mint is its use along with rosemary in vinegar as a hair rinse to help control dandruff.

Another decorative use of mint, especially the tall Applemint variety, is in floral arrangements with other herbs, such as chives, ornamentals and flowers.

Corsican Mint and Peppermint are particularly effective as insect repellents because of their high amount of strong, volatile oils. These oils are also long lasting. As a critter repellent, strew rodent-ridden areas with fresh Spearmint, Peppermint or Pennyroyal and watch the little feet fly.

Recipes

Spiced Mint Vinegar

Combine one cup **white wine vinegar** and one tablespoon sugar in a non-aluminum pan and heat to simmering point, but do not boil. Add one half teaspoon **vanilla.** Pour the vinegar mix over several six to eight inch sprigs of **mint,** one **stick of cinnamon,** three whole **cloves,** two whole **allspice,** and one strip of **orange peel** (1/2″ x 2 1/2″) in a clean bottle. Cap with plastic cap or cork and it will be ready to use in about one week.

This vinegar is especially good on coleslaw, or add a few drops to tomato juice or tomato aspic, or sprinkled over fresh fruit. This is my favorite vinegar for uncooked dishes.

Mint Tea

A good mint tea can be made from **Peppermint or Applemint.** Simply place a very generous handful of the freshly picked, washed and torn leaves into a hot china teapot, and cover with **boiling water.** Allow to steep about six to seven minutes and serve in a cup with a fresh leaf floating on top.

The color of this tea is a little strange, quite yellow, but the cooling menthol flavor will certainly perk up your day.

For each cup of Spearmint tea, place one tablespoon dried **Spearmint leaves** (or two to three tablespoon fresh) and one tablespoon **honey** in a pot with **boiling water.** Steep for five minutes, covered, and serve. Add a sprig of fresh mint for more aroma. This is a wonderful after dinner beverage.

Sleep Potion Sachet

Grind three cups each of **Spearmint,** and **rose petals or leaves,** and one ounce each of **cloves** and **orris root,** a fixative, together and place in a small bag. Use a pretty fabric such as lace, satin, silk, cotton or muslin about two to three inches square. Sew on three sides, turn and stuff with fragrance. Fringe or frilly lace may be sewn around the edge for decoration. Stitch the fourth side closed. Place on or under one layer of your pillow case for a refreshing night's sleep.

This herbal combination is used to treat insomnia and overcome melancholy. I buy small pieces of attractive fabric remnants and make these little bags as gifts, sometimes gifts for me!

Minted Honey

Use two to five tablespoons **fresh herbs** for a pint of **honey.** Bruise leaves slightly and place them in layers on the bottom of a saucepan. Pour room-temperature honey (unflavored) into the pan and heat over low. Stir just until honey is warm — about three minutes. Pour into jars and seal. Store for five days, rewarm honey and strain leaves out, if you wish.

I like this on biscuits, pancakes, peanut butter and honey sandwiches for kids, (or for me) or used in tea as a sweetener.

Mint and Pea Salad

Thaw one 10-ounce package of **small peas,** but do not cook them. Mix together a 'dressing' of two teaspoons **chopped chives,** one tablespoon each of **minced spearmint** and lemon juice, one half teaspoon **sugar,** one quarter cup each of **mayonnaise** and **sour cream** and one half cup **chopped cucumber.** Fold into the peas and chill an hour to blend the flavors.

Simple Herb Liqueur

Combine one and one half cups **sugar** and one quarter cup **water** in a saucepan and bring to a boil, stirring until sugar is completely dissolved. Pack two cups herbs (leaves and tender stems of Rose Geraniums, Lemon Balm, Lemon Verbena, mint, etc.) in a *large* glass container. Cool syrup to lukewarm and pour over herbs, then add one **liter of vodka.** Cap and store in a cool, dark place at least one month, shaking occasionally. Strain and decant into bottles.

This *liqueur* captures the flavor of fresh herb leaves, and is delicious with fruit or as a delicate *aperitif.*

Other Notes

Mint leaves are high in vitamins A and C, iron, calcium and riboflavin but lose some of their nutrition when heated over 100° F.

Peppermint purchased in the spice rack at a supermarket is one of the most expensive herbs per ounce of the commonly grown ones. You can save a bundle by growing your own.

Mint, especially Pennyroyal, is renowned for its insect-repelling qualities and used extensively in moth and flea chaser combinations. In your kitchen cupboard, mint will also deter mice and other rodents.

Mints attract bees much like Lemon Balm, which is almost reason enough to grow at least one.

Grasses and mints coexist well; neither seems to dominate the other. Planting Pennyroyal (a creeping mint) at the base of a tree can be done successfully even though a grassy area might be adjacent. The Pennyroyal will not invade the grassy areas like some other herb varieties.

Many mint species are grown almost exclusively in Australia and New Zealand because they are accommodated by these climates of cool summers and mild winters.

In talking with an avid mint grower recently, I learned that by placing fresh mint leaves in a bird bath, it will keep the water fresh and attractive to the birds.

Mints are like stray cats; you take them in, give them some food, and they are yours forever! I hope you will adopt one soon for your enjoyment.

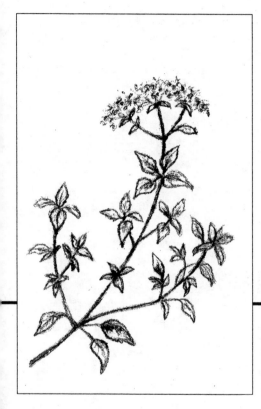

Oregano

*America's
Favorite Herb*

Oregano

When is oregano not oregano? When it's Sweet Marjoram. Gardeners selecting oregano or marjoram for an herb garden face a confusion of botanical and common names. This has frustrated botanists, nursery owners, and gardeners for years. Oregano is as much a flavor as it is a genus of herb. Basically, Sweet Marjoram and oregano are both species of _Origanum_ and have a similar taste. The essential difference for a gardener is that most oreganos are hardy perennials, while marjoram _Origanum majorana_ is a tender perennial, treated as an annual in areas where the temperature really drops each winter.

Common Oregano, _Origanum vulgare_, is the oregano most widely sold in nurseries and grown in gardens. You may also find some trailing oregano (also _O. vulgare_) with a more prostrate growing habit.

'Marjoram sings of sweet earth's flowers, while oregano summons the spicy powers.' The common name, oregano, describes more of a taste than a plant. Oregano derives its name from the Greek words 'oro' (mountain) and 'ganos' (joy). Its fresh fragrance and colorful flowers indeed call forth the 'joy of the mountains.' It is said that Aphrodite created oregano as a symbol for happiness.

📷 Botanical Name

The *Origanum* genus, like many culinary herbs, is a member of the *Labiatae*, or mint family. The varieties are as diverse in pungency as they are in leaf color, size, texture and growth habit. More than 40 plants in four botanical families are known as *Oregano*. A number of quite different genera contain species that possess the flavor that we identify as oregano by virtue of the presence of carvacrol and, to a lesser degree, thymol in their essential oil. For culinary use I prefer those species which contain only trace amounts of carvacrol and thymol.

Marjoram and oregano are listed together as they both belong to the genus Origanum; their flowers taste similar and they can be used interchangeably.

Common Oregano — *Origanum vulgare* — is a very hardy perennial which can grow several feet high. The flower blooms are pink to purplish in color. It is less compact than other species and spreads rapidly by rhizomes underground. It may become quite leggy when grown in rich soil with plenty of water; on the other hand, dry conditions cause it to grow more prostrate with a spicier flavor. This oregano grows wild in England where it's called Wild Marjoram or Pot Marjoram. It is the least desirable oregano for cooking because it has no real flavor.

Sweet Marjoram — *O. majorana* — is really an oregano but not generally thought of as one because of its mild flavor, but fairly strong scent for culinary uses. This tender perennial grows to fourteen inches in height in an upright manner. It needs protection at just 32° F. In our area it is grown as an annual.

Compact Greek Marjoram — *O. vulgare 'Compactum'* — is similar to Pot Marjoram in flavor and makes a great potted plant. It is a tender perennial growing about ten inches high with green leaves. There is also a white variegated form.

Creeping Golden Oregano — *O. vulgare 'Aureum'* — is a low-growing bush with bright golden-green leaves that fade to yellow-green in summer. Dark purple flowers bloom in late summer and dry well for crafts. This species tolerates summer's heat and endures mild winters. It spreads quickly to fill in cracks in rock gardens and makes a nice contrast plant in the landscape. Although this variety has a mild, savory flavor, it is also an inferior choice for culinary uses.

Greek Oregano — *O. heracleoticum* — is called Winter Marjoram in England. This species is a semi-evergreen plant that is slow growing and sometimes treated as a tender perennial. It has leaves that are slightly pointed, aromatic and hairy underneath with white edible flowers. This should not be confused with the common 'Pot Marjoram' so often substituted for it. True Greek Oregano has a strong flavor with a volatile and peppery taste. Known as the 'pizza herb' with spicy, aromatic leaves, the Greek Oregano is the most piquant and flavorful for cooking. This variety is good fresh or dried and can be used for decorative purposes as well.

'True' Greek Oregano — *O. onites* — has an even hotter flavor than Greek Oregano, and is called Rigani in Greece. This is sometimes called Pot Marjoram and can grow to two feet tall in its upright manner. The leaves are smaller, waxy, and a lighter pale green in color, but it has a distinctive sharp aroma that is preferred for most Greek dishes. The flowers are white or pink in color. It is not winter-hardy in cold climates, but will do well indoors during the winter.

Italian Oregano — *O. onites* — is a hybrid cross of Sweet Marjoram and Wild Oregano but is hardy to 0° F. This variety grows in clumps rather than spreading and has thin stems with small green leaves. It is sometimes sold as Hardy Marjoram. Because it's a hybrid and doesn't produce seeds, it must be grown from cuttings. Its aroma is a bit sharper than Sweet Marjoram and, therefore, is an excellent choice of a formal and herbaceous oregano if you prefer a less hot and harsh flavor.

Crinkle Leaf Oregano — *O. vulgare* 'Aureum Crispum' — is a compact form that seldom flowers. The golden leaves are quite curly and have a savory flavor. These leaves will scorch in the hot sun.

Turkish Oregano — *O. vulgare subspecies hirtum* — is most prominent in dried oregano purchased at the store. This species is used in native Greece as well as in Italy and France and is considered somewhat hardy. Its green leaves with a yellowish tinge produce a pungent flavor like a blend of Peppermint, pine, and clove oils. This 18 inch tall plant grows wild in Greece and has a spreading nature.

Dwarf Oregano — *O. vulgare microphyllum* — is a variety that is quite compact and well-behaved and usually planted in a front border. This variety is similar to *O. vulgare Compactum* — Compact Greek Marjoram.

Mexican Oregano — *Lippia graveolens* — is a cultivar that has long been prized for its especially spicy, earthy flavor. This is actually a member of the verbena family but is used in Mexico as oregano. Rodale's Illustrated Encyclopedia of Herbs describes it as a tender, deciduous, perennial shrub, four to six feet tall, which has become naturalized from the Texas-Mexico border to Central America. The aromatic, rough, and rounded leaves are pale green and bristly to the touch. These are usually used in the dried form. The plant blooms most of the year, especially after a rainfall, with yellowish white flowers clustered at the base of each set of opposite leaves. A tender perennial, it can only be grown outdoors in the South and Southwest. The species name, *graveolens,* means "strong smelling" and it is strong-tasting as well.

Dittany of Crete — *O. dictamnus* — is also known as Hop Marjoram and grows semi-upright in the garden with small, round, gray and woolly leaves. This legendary herb is a tender perennial about 12 inches tall. It produces drooping heads of tiny pink flowers in a head of green bracts during the late summer. 'Dittany' has a spicy pungency and is very decorative in the garden or in a container. Its taste is not as pungent. Although this variety is grown chiefly for decoration, its leaves can be eaten in salads or used as a substitute for other oreganos in tea. It is also one of the ingredients in vermouth.

Oregano, USCS — *Oregano 'USCS'* — is a tender ornamental oregano that resembles 'Dittany of Crete' and is used as a dried flower.

Spanish Oregano — *O. virens* — is a much milder flavored species of oregano and is gathered in the wild to dry for commercial purposes.

History

This native Portuguese and North African plant feels as much at home throughout the Southwest of North America as it does in Southern Europe and the Middle Eastern countries. The Mediterranean rocky soils, arid conditions, and relatively mild winters provide perfect growing conditions for this delightful herb, oregano. Its cultivation in central Europe and the Mediterranean area has been recorded for 12 centuries. Having a history 1300 years longer than marjoram, it has been historically used for medicinal purposes — from toothache to opium addiction.

The Spaniards and Italians began recording its use for cooking during the 14th century, especially in meat and vegetable stews and with shellfish. The Romans who recognized and chronicled the sensual delights of many plants, made sachets of oregano as well as rosemary and lavender to perfume linens and baths. Native Americans have known oregano-flavored herbs for generations and have used them as medicinal teas and as flavoring for meats.

Herbal remedies and robust dishes are associated with oregano, while Sweet Marjoram is surrounded by myths and is one of the most popular culinary herbs. Marjoram and oregano were used to flavor beer before people started using hops, and both were used as teas in England before Eastern teas were imported.

The oregano of commerce was once harvested from the wild in the mountains of Greece, but as the wild supplies became depleted there, the spice companies turned to Turkey. The peasants in that region gathered anything that smelled or looked remotely like an oregano. Therefore, the dried herb at the market is typically a variety of plants that generally smell like oregano, but is not necessarily of the *Origanum vulgare* species. These market products may contain Pennyroyal, Spearmint, Pot Marjoram, Lemon Balm and other varieties of herb plants.

People throughout the world have discovered totally different plants which yield the same oregano flavor. They are searching for a similar taste that they had previously experienced. Perhaps humans possess a genetic memory for tastes and flavors passed on from our ancient ancestors. There are plants growing almost everywhere that taste similar to each other, so we can all satisfy our deep-down yearning for our remembrance of good tastes. Isn't that convenient!

Oregano came to North America with various European colonists and escaped from their gardens to grow wild. These oregano plants became standard medicines in the United States and were listed in various books as a stimulant. Since World War II, spice merchants began promoting and importing oregano in great quantities. During this same time, servicemen returned from the Mediterranean with a taste for oregano, and it became embedded into the American consciousness as the 'pizza herb.' Oregano has moved from obscurity to its position as one of the most popular dried herbs in the United States.

Since the late 1960's, many Americans have been changing their attitudes about health and healing. Many of us retired our salt shakers and rediscovered culinary herbs and spices. The United States has been importing thousands of tons of oregano since 1959 and the numbers have grown substantially since that time.

 ## TYPE: Perennial *(hardy)*

Many oregano species are perennial plants fairly hardy to 0° F. Other varieties as mentioned above are considered much more tender in our Pacific Northwest climate. Each individual herb gardener can find an oregano that will do well where you live and survive for many years. They are well worth growing.

Description

Oreganos are aromatic, herbaceous perennials with erect, hairy, square stems which are slightly woody. This small shrub-like plant is a real sun-lover that's partial to well-drained loamy soil. Even grown in containers, oregano spreads rapidly and is self-sowing. They grow from 10-24 inches tall — some erect and some more prostrate. These more prostrate varieties make attractive low spreading mounds and are quite carefree. The Common and Greek Oreganos reach at least two feet; whereas, marjoram grows just one to two feet high, and tends to prefer slightly damper conditions. Most oreganos send up vertical flowering stems above a mat of foliage close to the ground.

The leaves of oregano plants are oval to elliptical in shape and generally slightly hairy underneath with a lively and aromatic scent. The leaves are from mid to dark green, and sometimes a gray, depending on the variety. The flowers are one-quarter inch long, tubular in shape in terminal spikelets and bloom July through September. These flowers range in color from white to mauvish-purple. Wild Marjoram usually has pink flowers and purple bracts, and Greek or Turkish Oregano generally has white flowers and green bracts.

These mostly hardy perennials are not clearly defined by herbal authorities as mentioned earlier. The oreganos and marjorams are closely related but the varieties are different in growth and flavor. It is the leaves of this perennial plant that are dried and sold as ground oregano.

What about Greek Oregano? This *common name* is usually associated with __Origanum heracleoticum__ and __Origanum vulgare__. Because these varieties have more oil glands in their leaves, they have a stronger flavor with bitter undertones. Fresh oregano has a spicy fragrance with hints of clove and balsam. Wild Marjoram has a weak, musty smell while True Greek or Turkish Oregano has a very pungent, penetrating smell, almost like creosote.

Planting & Care Requirements

Fast draining soil that is sweet and gritty and all the sunlight they can get is the formula for successful oregano growing. These plants will tolerate some shade but you will forfeit a loss of the flavor in the leaves. Some herb gardeners protect the golden leaf varieties from hot afternoon sun which they believe helps preserve the leaf color. An alkaline soil with a pH 6.8 is desirable and dryish conditions are optimum. With its robust growing habit, good drainage is imperative to prevent root rot, and this can be achieved by adding copious amounts of humus or other organic material to the planting soil. Origanums have more colorful flowers and more fragrant leaves if they get full sun for at least half a day.

Although oregano does best in a sunny spot in fast-draining, weed-free soil, it has its best flavor from arid conditions. Once established, it takes only moderate watering. The plants do need space around them for their fine-branching lateral roots which tend to creep. Fertilizing the plants about once a month with a fish emulsion when they are getting established will help these roots develop. Once established in the garden, however, oreganos require little special attention assuming, of course, that plenty of nutrients are available in the soil.

Some of the spiciest and most flavorful oreganos thrive in these poorer and drier conditions. Over-watering and fertilization with soil that is too rich may produce large leaves but these will have little taste and these conditions may even promote root disease. Because these plants are susceptible to both root rot and fungal disease, good drainage becomes particularly important.

Some spider mite damage may occur during high heat and humidity, but the use of an insecticidal soap is usually enough of a deterrent. Leaf miners sometimes chew serpentine patterns in leaves but these, too, can be controlled with the soap. Leaf miner eggs are usually visible on the back of the leaves as small, white clusters. A protective screening, such as Reemay, can be used to prevent the egg-laying from adults reaching the leaves. The strong odor of oregano will deter most insects away from these plants.

Foliage of this herb tastes sweeter if the flowers are not allowed to develop. To prevent flowering and to keep the plants from becoming woody, trim them regularly. Oregano is not particularly fussy, but the growth should be pinched back before they flower as this will increase the strength in the stems as well promote lateral branching. This pinching back of the tips or harvesting sprigs to be used in cooking will keep your plant bushy and productive.

Oregano varieties seem to survive much colder temperatures in the arid western United States than in humid gardens of the East Coast. They grow wild very willingly in open, rocky hillsides.

 **Harvesting**

Although fresh young leaves can be picked at anytime, harvest oregano twice a year — once in June before flowering, and then later in the fall. This early summer harvesting will produce sweeter-tasting leaves and usually occurs about two months after the growth first begins. You can begin harvesting the sprigs when they are only six inches tall. In June, when the plant is budding so vigorously that it's hard to keep them picked, cut the whole plant, leaving only the lowest set of leaves — about six inches above ground. Using this pruning method, cut the full branches of pungent leaves. It sounds rash, but the plant will start leafing out again within two weeks producing handsome, bushy little plants. If your oregano plants are older, you may wish to prune just half to three-quarters of the bush at a time because of the extra woody stems.

The second harvest can be accomplished in August. This fall harvest should be less drastic to avoid freeze damage. Be sure that there is six or seven weeks of fall weather remaining before the hard freeze is expected. Although oregano generally dies back in the winter, it will return again in the early spring.

If harvesting leaves for preserving, gather them just before the flowers open. For harvesting marjoram, cut the plants back by two-thirds before they die down in the winter.

Common, Greek, and Trailing Oreganos sometimes need replanting every three years for the most successful and flavorful harvests.

Preservation

When considering the best method of preserving oregano, I typically choose to create several bottles of vinegar to save the bounteous harvest. The remainder is then dried in my dehydrator as it retains the most intense flavor with this type of preservation. Bruised oregano leaves preserved in oil is also a good way of enjoying the intense flavor all winter long. Be sure that any oils are kept refrigerated!

To dry, the plant's stems may be cut as soon as the flowers appear or before. Drying improves the flavor of all kinds of oreganos as well as both Sweet and Wild Marjoram. Oregano dries easily by hanging in bunches or by placing in the microwave. For air drying, after cutting and rinsing the stems and leaves, hang them upside down in small bunches. These bunches need to be protected from dust, moisture, and light as I explained earlier in this book regarding lavender. For the dehydrator or microwave method, the whole stems or individual leaves can be laid on paper toweling in the oven or on non-metal screens.

The leaves may be used fresh all summer long, but many cooks prefer dried oregano to the fresh because of its intensified flavor. I use both fresh and dried oregano because I like the contrast the different textures create in various dishes and during different seasons of the year.

The leaves of oregano (and marjoram) also freeze very well. Follow the same instructions for freezing basil in chapter one.

🌱 Propagation

Seeds of oregano plants are not absolute as to precise variety. In fact, some seed packets will actually have a mix of oregano species in a packet. For this reason, I don't recommend starting oregano from seed. If you must resort to seed, however, plant a lot so you can select the plants with prime flavor when they are large enough to taste. Discard the others or use in a *potpourri* or sachet. Strongly flavored varieties are apparent even when the plants are young.

The seeds are tiny, dark brown, and tear-shaped. Don't cover them with soil as they germinate better in light. If seeds are kept at the optimum germination temperature of 70° F., they should germinate in four to eight days. Thin or transplant the seedlings when they are two to three inches tall, and replant them 8-15 inches apart. Once these seedlings are established, be sure to keep them a little on the dry side.

Often young plants from nurseries are labeled incorrectly, especially if started from seed; therefore, it is safest to start your oregano from divisions or cuttings to get the exact variety you desire. These cuttings or root divisions can be done in the spring. Adding cuttings taken from the plants you like best for flavor and aroma is a superb way of increasing your stock. This will prevent you from accidently acquiring an unwanted 'common oregano' when you really expected a true Greek variety. For a good selection of oreganos, one or two of each of several species per garden is suggested.

Division of the plants by the roots every few years ensures a more flavorful herb as well as increasing your stock. This is a good time to remove dead and woody branches as well. These divisions can be taken in early spring or in the fall. Older plants are less flavorful and can be divided every two or three years to renew their vigor. By dividing you can discard the older center part and replant the younger parts from the edge of the clump.

When these new cuttings or divisions are six inches tall, pinch back the tops to encourage branching and bushy growth. Frequently cutting back new growth and pinching off the flowers also promote good growth and flavor.

One of the easiest ways to propagate oregano is simply by layering. The horizontal stems will root wherever they touch the soil if left for a few days. My spreading varieties do this very nicely without help from me and I then have an ample supply to put into four inch pots for friends or plant sales.

🍴 Culinary Uses

Piquant, aromatic oregano is the wherewithal for many savory dishes. It is sometimes referred to as Wild Marjoram. All marjoram species are also called oregano, but only a few of the 50 plants called oregano are ever called marjoram. It sounds confusing, and it certainly can be. Try to use the botanical name whenever possible.

Oregano is known as the 'soul of Italian cooking,' and it's also the most important seasoning in many Mexican, Greek, Cuban, Columbian and Spanish dishes. Greeks adore oregano and sprinkle it over *souvlaki*, tender chunks of marinated beef. Spaniards smother grilled fish with a thick green oregano sauce. Middle Easterners flavor eggplant and other vegetables with this pungent herb, while Mexicans add it to their spicy chile sauces and stews. Of course, Italians revere oregano, using it in hearty tomato sauces and pasta dishes.

Oregano's most popular use in the United States is as the beloved pizza herb. It also gives character to meat loaf, stew, *chili con carne*, potatoes, and tomatoes. In addition, it is equally at home in homemade soups, roast meats, sprinkled on seafood or green salads, added to baked beans, or cheese dishes. Oregano is also wonderful with almost any tomato dish.

Unlike the dried oregano herb you are accustomed to using from the market, fresh garden oregano brings a more intense, delightful flavor to cooking. It has a unique taste that rises head and shoulders above the store-bought variety whether it is used fresh, dried or frozen. Its strong, aromatic flavor has a pleasant bitter undertone.

Oregano is considered a medium-flavored herb along with basil, dill, tarragon, marjoram, mint, savory and thyme. The spicy 'true oregano', or Mexican Oregano, however, will really add zest to a wide variety of dishes. Their hot spicy flavors complement and add special magic to minestrone or any bean soup and makes roast lamb or chicken a Mediterranean delight. Add a few sprigs to your next fish or seafood dish, and you'll have a creation to remember. Enliven a simple steamed vegetable — green beans, zucchini, eggplant or acorn squash — with oregano. Its unusual zest should be tried in deviled eggs or make your own herb bread or herb butter seasoned with oregano. Stuff a whole fish with oregano and a few slices of lime or lemon and onion before baking or grilling. Making gallons of oregano vinegar in the fall will preserve this abundant harvest and have lots of wonderful uses all winter long.

Different varieties of oregano in Italian recipes, salad dressings, meats, vegetables, breads, cheese, eggs, lamb, poultry, sauces, stews, herb butters, herbed olive oil and vinegars are all delightful. I make my oregano herb vinegar in combination with chilies, garlic, and cider vinegar. Oregano and parsley make good partners when combined with garlic and olive oil as a sauce for fish. An oregano *pesto* is great with pasta and goat cheese. Use the recipe in the basil chapter for *pesto,* but substitute two cups of fresh oregano, loosely packed, and one cup fresh parsley for the basil. Use lime zest and one teaspoon lime juice for additional zingy flavor.

The flowers of oregano and marjoram are spicy with a sweet perfume. However, the marjoram flowers are milder, sweeter, and less pungent, while oregano flowers are heavier tasting, hot, and spicier. These flowers are compatible with all sorts of food — vegetables, cheeses, meat and poultry. They also add a lovely garnish to salads, pizza, pasta and many Italian-style dishes. Rinse and dry the flowers before using. Pull or snip these individual florets from the stems. They can be coarsely chopped or used whole.

My 'biker neighbor,' Fuzzy Fletcher, is an oregano aficionado of the highest order. He adds oregano to his homemade yeast breads for dimension and serves himself a baked potato smothered with oregano instead of chives. A little sour cream on the side helps the oregano go down! I prefer my oregano on marinated chicken breast and vegetables, especially mushrooms. You might want to try my marinade by combining oregano with garlic, thyme, parsley, and olive oil. Try Fuzzy's baked potato — better yet, try both!

 # Medicinal Uses

Traditional Chinese physicians have used oregano for centuries to treat fever, vomiting, diarrhea, jaundice, and itching skin conditions. Greeks have made poultices from the leaves and placed them on sores and aching muscles. Europeans used it as a digestive aid, arthritis treatment, expectorant for cough, colds, flu, and chest congestion, and as a menstruation promoter. American 19th century physicians considered oregano a gently stimulating tonic, and other folk healers used oregano oil to treat earache and toothache. Next time you have a cough or bronchitis, try a pizza with extra oregano. If it doesn't help, at least it will taste good.

All the oreganos contain a volatile oil high in two chemically related expectorants — carvacrol and thymol. These help loosen phlegm and make it easier to cough up; lending credence to the herb's traditional use in colds, flu, and chest congestion. Carvacrol, a phenol, has been accepted as an antiseptic for many years and valued in the treatment of skin diseases as well as a warming ingredient in liniment used for rheumatic pain and arthritis.

Like most culinary herbs, oregano helps soothe the smooth muscle lining of the digestive tract, making it an antispasmodic. It may also help expel parasitic intestinal worms. With its long history of varied uses as a medicinal tea for general complaints, oregano is used as a warm, aromatic, spicy infusion to settle the stomach or treat a cold. An infusion of oregano flowers served as a tea reportedly helps to prevent seasickness, colds and headaches. In fact, just sniffing it can help dissipate a headache.

Gargling this infusion can be soothing for sore throats or used as a mouth wash. Try chewing a couple of oregano leaves to relieve a toothache. For a therapeutic herbal tea, use one to two teaspoons of dried herb per cup of boiling water and steep for ten minutes. You may drink up to three cups a day. Sweet Marjoram, on the other hand, makes a soothing tea. *Do not give these infusions to children under the age of two years.*

As a tonic or stimulant, oregano can be effective, but in larger doses it can actually cause drowsiness. Traditionally, the tonics were employed as a respiratory sedative. Since this herb genus has antioxidant properties, it is a potential candidate for increased use in the food industry.

All oreganos are considered safe in amounts typically recommended, but pregnant or nursing mothers should not ingest great amounts.

[?] Other Uses

For cosmetic uses, oregano is used extensively in the perfume industry.

Try a handful of oregano leaves in a muslin bag in a steaming hot bath for a soothing relief of aching joints. I enjoy this especially for my arthritis. Or you might want to place dried oregano flowers along with other herbs in a soft, thin case for a sleep pillow. It really does promote a restful night.

Many gardeners grow this species *(Origanum vulgare)* for its ornamental lavender flowers that dry well and are often used as a pretty garnish on plates and platters.

For decorative uses, clusters of dried oregano stems are wonderful in floral arrangements or as additions to wreaths. I use these in conjunction with garden sage and thyme bunches as the wreath background on a moss, wire wound circle. The addition of fresh oregano in a living culinary wreath is popular as a kitchen gift. Oregano and marjoram leaves and flowers are both superb as *potpourri* ingredients.

Shrubby oregano branches can be soaked in water (to keep the woody stems from burning) and placed directly on hot coals of a barbecue. This will contribute a distinctive flavor to the overall smoky taste of your entree.

 **Recipes**

Below are listed three main dish recipes using oregano, two of which are vegetarian. One is a pizza you might want to try, but all are my favorites. I eat a lot of homemade soup because of the wonderful blend of flavors of vegetables and herbs. I hope you like the black bean stew and my best minestrone recipe!

Barbecue Blend

For this favorite herb blend, I use fairly equal amounts of **cumin** and **oregano** (lightly crushed), with a smaller amount of minced **garlic** and a little **hot pepper sauce,** or ground red pepper. Go lightly on the pepper until you create a combination that suits your particular tastes. This barbecue blend can be mixed with **olive oil** and used as a marinade on hamburgers, chicken, or spare ribs.

Black Bean Stew

Bring two cups **black beans** (previously soaked overnight, drained and rinsed) to a boil in four cups fresh **water** (or two cups water and two cups of **unsalted chicken stock**). Add one medium **onion**, chopped; one stalk of **celery,** chopped; two cloves of minced **garlic;** one half of a **green pepper**, chopped; one tablespoon of **dark sesame oil;** one tablespoon **miso paste;** one teaspoon **dried oregano** (or one tablespoon fresh); one half teaspoon crushed **cumin** and a dash of **tabasco.** Simmer until the beans are soft, about one and one half to two hours. Add one half cup crushed **tomatoes** (canned or fresh), one tablespoon **rum** (optional), and one tablespoon fresh

lemon juice and cook another 30 minutes. Leave the lid off to reduce and thicken the liquid. Remove one cup of bean mixture and puree in a blender and return to the pot. Just before serving, sprinkle with one tablespoon each of chopped **cilantro** and chopped **parsley**. If you wish to add any salt to this recipe do it at the end. Salting the beans earlier will prevent them softening when they cook.

These beans are also known as turtle beans or mock turtle beans and are very flavorful and nutritious. Oregano is wonderful in any bean recipe. A couple of ways to help prevent flatulence from beans is to soak the beans for up to three days before cooking (changing the water several times), or adding the herb *epazote* (Mexican tea) during the last 15 minutes of cooking. Also, a new product called BEANO is available in health food stores and works quite well. Don't let flatulence stop you from eating beans and legumes. They are so high in nutrition and low in calories with lots of fiber and flavor.

Salad Dressing

Mix two tablespoons **tomato juice** and one tablespoon **water** in a cruet. Add one clove of minced **garlic**, a pinch of **cayenne pepper**, two teaspoons fresh chopped **oregano** and one teaspoon fresh chopped **parsley**. Shake and chill for one hour before serving as a dressing.

This is such a simple and fresh-tasting dressing, it is served often in my home. Try it on cold green beans or asparagus. I also like it on lightly steamed zucchini slices and sprinkled with a bit of Parmesan cheese.

Minestrone

Sauté one half pound homemade **sausage** over medium heat, drain and reserve. With a small amount of **olive oil** in a cast iron Dutch oven, sauté two stalks of chopped **celery**, two large **carrots**, chopped, one large chopped **potato**, three cloves of chopped **garlic**, and one large Walla Walla **onion** (lucky you if you have access to these sweet beauties from Washington State). Cook gently for about five minutes on medium heat. Add 14-16 ounces of home-canned or purchased **tomatoes** (I like Roma type) and one and one half quarts of **chicken or vegetable stock.** Cook about 20 minutes over simmer and add one medium **zucchini** sliced, one cup fresh **green beans** cut in one inch lengths, one pound of **green's stems** (I like Swiss Chard or Chinese Cabbage) and cook another five minutes. Add reserved sausage, one cup cooked **cannellini beans (white kidney beans)** and one half cup of small **pasta,** dried (shell or elbow). Cook additional ten minutes and lastly add the herbs. One tablespoon fresh **marjoram,** two tablespoons fresh **oregano,** two teaspoons fresh **basil** and a little **salt and pepper** to taste. Turn off the heat and let stand 20 minutes to mix flavors. Serve hot with grated **Parmesan** or *pesto* on the top.

This is a one-dish meal that will serve six to eight healthy appetites. My minestrone is very individual, like most. I always use fresh vegetables (rather than canned or frozen) because they are more appealing and keep their crispness. I use vegetables in season and always include onions, carrots, garlic and greens of some kind, along with a tomato product and sausage. Basil and oregano are the two prominent herbs for minestrone.

Vegetarian Eggplant Pizza With Oregano

Wash, peel and cut one medium **eggplant** into crosswise slices one half inch thick. **Salt** the slices lightly and place in a colander to drain while making the sauce. This step will remove the bitter flavor that is disagreeable to some people.

Heat two tablespoons **olive oil** in a saucepan and add one clove of **minced garlic,** one half cup each of chopped **onion** and chopped **green or red pepper.** Cook over medium heat, stirring for three minutes. Add four and one half tablespoons **tomato paste** (or one to two fresh Roma-type tomatoes, cored and crushed) and three tablespoons of **water.** Cover and cook, stirring, over low heat until very thick — about ten minutes. Add one teaspoon each of dried **oregano,** dried **basil** and **sugar** and a pinch of **salt** at end of cooking time. Remove from heat and set aside.

Beat one **egg** with one tablespoon **milk** and set aside. Mix one half cup fine **dry bread crumbs** with one third cup grated **Parmesan cheese** and one quarter teaspoon **black pepper.** Rinse and pat the eggplant dry. Dip the eggplant slices in **flour** for dredging, then in the beaten egg, then in the seasoned bread crumbs. Saute the eggplant slices in hot (but not smoking) **peanut or olive oil or butter** until golden, turning to brown both sides. Remove from the skillet and drain well on paper toweling.

Place sauteed eggplant slices on a cookie sheet and spread them with cooked tomato mixture. Top with sliced **mozzarella cheese,** chopped **olives** and **basil or oregano** leaves. Place under the broiler until cheese has melted and is lightly browned. Makes six delicious pizza servings.

Baked Mushrooms with Oregano

Sauté two finely chopped Walla Walla (or other sweet) **onions** in six tablespoons of **butter** for ten minutes, stirring frequently. Combine one cup of **milk,** one cup of **half-and-half** and two cups of fresh or dried **bread crumbs.** Allow crumbs to absorb liquid. Combine the onions with the crumb mixture and add to two pounds of finely chopped **mushrooms,** a little **salt and pepper,** one teaspoon of fresh chopped **oregano** (or one half teaspoon dried) and three well-beaten **eggs.** Mix well and pour into buttered bread loaf pan. Bake at 350° F. for one hour. Slice and serve. Serves six to eight.

This is a good side dish to any poultry entree.

✍ Other Notes

One unique use for oregano I discovered was in making a gentleman's cosmetic. Bald men mixed oregano with olive oil and rubbed it, with hope surging, into their scalps, to hasten hair growth. It has never, however, been documented that this oregano poultice actually grew new hair on bald heads.

The leaves of oregano were rubbed over heavy oak furniture and floors to give a fragrant polish in the Middle Ages. It is also effective as a moth repellent in a small bag placed in closets.

In the Colonial era of America, the ladies used oregano as a dying base for woolens and linen.

Even though this plant suffers from an identity crisis — so many species and subspecies that are similar — it certainly is a must in your herb garden. I can't imagine having my pizza and other Italian food without this wonderful pungent herb.

Parsley

The Utility Player

Parsley

Did your Mother ever say to you, "Eat your parsley, it's good for you. It has lots of vitamins?" My Mother did, but to me it just looked like little bushes on my plate that were fun to play with. Ogden Nash stated that, "parsley is gharsley." Fortunately, I grew up and have learned to really appreciate this flavorful, albeit ubiquitous, herb. I find its clean, crisp taste most appealing and love to munch on it in the garden — especially if I have had garlic in the last few hours. It tends to be 'user friendly' to garlic lovers.

In the language of herbs, parsley means feasting, death, or joy. Having dual symbolism, it is said to signify both revelry and victory. In mythology, parsley supposedly sprang from the blood of Archemnorus, a Greek hero, and subsequently garlands of parsley were used to crown champions at the Isthmian games.

Parsley is one of the first herbs to appear in the spring and has been used for centuries in the Seder, the ritual Jewish Passover meal, as a symbol of new beginnings. Parsley can be used fresh most of the year, as it is very hardy. It's also lovely in hanging baskets for indoor gardens.

Parsley is a member of the _Apiaceae_ or _Umbelliferae_ family along with carrots, celery, dill, cilantro, and caraway.

119

Botanical Name

Common Parsley is sold as <u>*Petroselinum crispum,*</u> <u>*Petroselinum hortense*</u>, or <u>*Petroselinum sativum*</u>, and sometimes as Rock Selinon.

French or Curly Parsley — <u>*Petroselinum crispum*</u> — leaves are tightly curled and fringed into bright green clumps on strong stems. Some varieties of this most commonly used herb include Moss Curled and Triple Curled. Danish Afro has highly curled and fringed leaves on strong stems. Its crisp, lacy, leaves have a very sweet flavor, without the bitter, metallic overtones of some other Curly Parsley. This variety also rarely gets mildewed in rainy weather. Sometimes Curly-Leafed Parsleys taste slightly salty and even bitter.

Italian or Genovese Parsley — <u>*Petroselinum crispum*</u> var. '*Neopolitanum*' — is a flat-leafed variety that has dark green, glossy leaves resembling those of celery. Most chefs (and we ordinary cooks) agree that this flat-leafed variety is the best cooking parsley, with its sweet, earthy, and regal flavor. This giant Italian Parsley's seeds often germinate more rapidly than Curly Parsley's. An Italian Parsley strain called Catalogna is handsome with celery-like foliage and is more fully flavored. (Italians call this herb *pressemolo gigante d'Italia vero Catalogno*.) It's a giant strain, and in comparison, makes other flat-leaved parsley taste flavorless. It must be grown from seed, however, as it's rarely available in bunches in the market. The stems of flat-leafed parsleys are particularly succulent and should be saved for cooking purposes or eaten like celery.

Hamburg Parsley — <u>*Petroselinum crispum or tubersosum*</u> —is a turnip-rooted parsley used like a parsnip. Its eight to ten inch white roots are used as a flavorful vegetable, while its leaves are used in the same ways as the other types of parsley. Harvest the root in its second year.

Japanese Parsley 'Mitsuba' — <u>*Cryptotaenia canadensis (japonica)*</u> — is a perennial herb used frequently for stir-fry, floated on miso soup or in sauce for Japanese noodles. Although this is not a true parsley and is sometimes called White Chervil, its flavor is stronger than Curly Parsley but also has a subtle hint of celery. This variety can be used like any parsley. The plant is an interesting foliage plant as the tiny blossoms appear an inch or two from the soil surface on the lower part of the stems as the fruit (seed pods) ripens.

Chervil, Beaked or French Parsley — *Anthriscus cerefolium* — is actually chervil, an annual that has parsley-flavored leaves. It is a member of the parsley family and its lacy leaves resemble those of parsley but are a lighter green and more feathery. This plant grows about eight inches tall and likes some shade, thriving under taller plants. (A substitute for chervil in a recipe can be two parts of parsley to one part of tarragon.)

Mexican Parsley — Cilantro is used widely in Latin America. See: Chinese Parsley/Coriander.

Chinese Parsley — *Coriandrum sativum* — is an annual plant whose lemony-flavored seeds (from the Cilantro plant) are widely used in baking and in special mixtures, such as curry powder. Because it's popular in the Orient as a leafy herb used fresh, it is known as Chinese Parsley. It tastes like a blend of lemon and parsley. Generally, the foliage is known as Cilantro and the dried seeds as Coriander, and each has a distinctively different flavor. It was said to have aphrodisiac qualities in the Middle Ages and was added to love potions.

History

Native to the Mediterranean, parsley has a long history of being appreciated. The Romans served parsley at feasts to cleanse and refresh the palate. They also used this herb at orgies to cover up the smell of alcohol on the breath, while it also aided their digestion. The Greeks and Romans thought parsley to be an antidote to poison, so it was placed on the dish symbolically as a token of trust. To eat the parsley in those days would have cast aspersions on the friendly intentions of the host.

Although the Romans were the first people recorded as eating parsley, the Greeks a thousand years before made wreaths of it for weddings and athletic games. They also fed it to their horses before battle to ensure their steed's valor and stamina. For centuries, Greek soldiers believed any contact with parsley before battle signaled impending death. Because of its association with death, parsley was planted on Greek graves. The Greeks also used parsley in funeral ceremonies long before it was thought of as a garnish...probably to deodorize the bodies.

Ironically, this custom led to its reclamation. Because the Greek God, Hercules, had chosen parsley for his garlands, it was placed in wreaths given to winning athletes. Athletic contests were held to honor the memory of important figures, and the winners were rewarded with parsley wreaths. At festivals, youths and maidens wore ceremonial garlands of herbs, including parsley, dill and fennel. As its cultivation spread throughout Europe and Asia Minor, parsley became one of the most popular culinary herbs.

Over the centuries, the herb came to symbolize strength. But the shadow of bad luck clung to the herb well into the Middle Ages. At that time Europeans considered it a Devil's herb, sure to bring disaster upon those who grew it — unless they planted it on Good Friday. Because of this belief, it was associated with oblivion and death.

By the Middle Ages, parsley had made its appearance in herbal medicines. It was given credit for curing a great range of human ills. Parsley has been used to fight The Plague, asthma, dropsy, and jaundice, and especially problems having to do with the kidneys, liver, and bladder.

The word 'parsley' comes from the Greek PETROS, 'rock,' referring to its rocky wild habitat. Because of the Greek custom of bordering their gardens with parsley and rue, there is a beguiling expression, no longer current, which says, "we are at the parsley and the rue." This meant, being at the beginning of a project.

According to legend, parsley sprang up from the blood of Opheltes, infant son of King Lycurgus of Nemea. The boy was killed by a serpent while his Nanny directed some thirsty soldiers to a spring.

The Romans transported the herb to Britain, and at one time, a parsley patch was part of every English garden, and often children were told that it was their place of origin. The Renaissance herbalists of England had a wealth of medicinal uses for it, as well as advice on when and how to plant it.

Medieval Germans used parsley compresses for arthritis, inflamed eyes and black-and-blue marks. Parsley boiled in wine was used for chest and heart pain.

Parsley grows wild from Sardinia east to Lebanon. It is cultivated throughout the temperate zones, including the United States.

In America from 1850 to 1926, parsley was used as a laxative, a diuretic for kidney problems and fluid accumulation due to congestive heart failure, and as a substitute for quinine to treat malaria. After 1926, man-made drugs were used in its place.

About one quarter of the spices consumed in the United States from 1970-75 were grown here rather than in the tropics. This included parsley, along with basil, sage, mustard seed, dill, fennel and sesame. The modern interest in herbs undoubtedly arises partly from a new consciousness of nature and a desire to return to a more natural way of life. It also stems from the blandness and sameness of modern foods and a desire to stretch ordinary budgets and ingredients into gourmet meals at home. Parsley has been at the head of the class for these uses.

No gardening offers such great rewards for such little work as growing herbs, especially parsley. It should be a main ingredient of a basic herb garden, along with basil, savory, sage, marjoram, and chives.

 **TYPE: Biennial** *(hardy)*

A biennial plant takes two years to complete its life cycle. The first year it grows roots and leaves. The second year, having died to the ground during winter's cold, it sends up two-foot tall flower stalks, and their blossoms ripen into brown seeds that will remain viable for a period of two or three years. If the summers are hot, the plant often becomes rather puny and loses its flavor for culinary uses. You may want to treat parsley as an annual and start with fresh seed in the fall. However, I let my parsley flower in the second year to collect its seeds. These are used to start new plants as well as for a number of medicinal and cosmetic purposes.

Description

Like mint, parsley is one of the easiest herbs to grow. It's cultivated for the leaves that it produces during its first year when the plant sends up a foliage tuft 8-12 inches and of equal spread. If not removed, the plant will send up its two-foot stalk during the second year and bear clusters of tiny, greenish flowers in early summer. The flowers, in turn, produce the brown seeds. Parsley has a thick carrot-like taproot and juicy stems terminating in feathery, deeply divided, curly or flat leaves, depending on the variety.

The most popular kind of parsley is that with curly foliage. Some good varieties are 'Champion Moss Curled' and 'Perfection.' If flat-leaved parsley is desired, 'Plain Italian Dark Green' is a good choice. A single mature plant of either type produces about one cup of leaves in three weeks. Don't pick *wild parsley* because it closely resembles three potentially lethal plants: water hemlock, poison parsley (also known as poison hemlock), and fool's parsley (dog parsley, small hemlock).

Parsley's taste is a faintly peppery tang with a green apple aftertaste. The brilliance of its emerald leaves and its mild yet piquant flavor have made it a standard whether as a garnish, flavoring, or meal accompaniment. It is a pleasant counter-point to most vegetables, fish, and meats.

Curly Parsley looks particularly good in hanging baskets, window sill planters and strawberry jar planters, and makes a very good edging plant in the garden.

 ## Planting & Care Requirements

Parsley grows best in full sun, (at least five hours of direct sunlight a day) but will tolerate light shade. Some shade will produce longer stems and a deeper green color to the leaves. The soil should be rich, moist and well-drained. Enrich the soil with compost or manure to achieve a pH 5.0 to 7.0 balance. The most important factor when growing parsley is *the soil*.

In most parts of the country, sow parsley seeds in very early spring for a summer crop or in late fall just before the ground freezes for a spring crop. When the seedlings are about two inches high, remove smaller ones to space plants three inches apart. When the plants have grown enough to touch one another, pull and use alternate plants; repeat when they touch again, making the final spacing 12 inches. Because parsley has a taproot, it should not be moved after this point. Plants with taproots do not transplant very well once they are established.

When the plants are four inches tall and again at six to eight inches, feed with 5-10-5 fertilizer at the rate of three ounces per ten foot row. Occasional light feedings of fish emulsion or manure can be helpful as well as composting mulch, especially during a cold winter or very warm summer. Leaves on developing parsley plants may be picked at any time.

All varieties of parsley can be grown as mid-size border plants arranged alternately with chives for a very attractive and eye-catching display. The foliage makes a delightful low border. Weed often and thoroughly to keep parsley productive.

In late spring and summer, beware of the 'parsleyworm,' the larval caterpillar of the swallow-tail butterfly, which quickly devours plants in the *Apiaceae* family. However, if you want to be a good neighbor you can share your parsley with this beautiful friend who will reward you later when he develops into his true magnificence. My solution is to simply pick the critters off and place in another area or destroy them. If you must, however, parsleyworm may be treated with b.t., a bacterial insecticide that is a stomach poison, not a contact poison. Parsley can also be susceptible to crown rot, carrot weevils, or nematodes. Spider mites and aphids may be treated with insecticidal soap.

If you wish to grow parsley in pots year around, fill four-inch pots with packaged potting soil and plant three seeds in each one, barely covering them with soil. Set the pots in a shady part of the garden and keep the soil moistened until the seeds germinate. Then move the pots into full sun and let the seedlings grow to about one inch in height before thinning out *all but the largest one* in each pot. Leave the pots outdoors until just before frost so that the plants will be growing as vigorously as possible when they are moved inside. Indoor parsley needs 12 hours a day of artificial light and they do best in day temperatures below 70° F.

For fresh parsley in winter, pot a growing plant from the garden. Begin the move early by digging up the entire plant in late summer with a generous ball of soil around its taproot. Set each plant into a six-inch pot and cut back the top foliage by about half to balance the loss of roots damaged in the digging. Keep the plants in the shade of a tree for a week or so until the leaves stop wilting. Then gradually give the plant more hours of direct sunlight each day. During this adjustment period, new roots will form and the herbs should be ready to be moved into the house early in the fall. Parsley can be grown in either clay or plastic pots, but good drainage is so important that I prefer to use unglazed clay pots even though their porous sides make watering more of a chore.

If starting parsley from a nursery plant, choose one that is very small (not root-bound) and with no yellowing of the bottom leaves. If there are many seedlings per pot, remove all but two or three of the largest. Sometimes it is necessary to remove the parsley, roots, and soil entirely from the pot to separate them carefully. Replant only one or two per pot. When these seedlings are four inches tall, you can transplant them to your outdoor garden spot.

Harvesting

Because of its growing habit, parsley sends up clumps of leaves or grasslike spears directly from its roots. Do not snip off the tops, giving the plant a "haircut," because repeated harvesting in this way will shear it progressively closer to the ground. This not only reduces the leaves to unsightly, yellow-tipped stubble but also prevents them from manufacturing the food supply to be stored in the roots over the winter so they will have enough energy to sprout vigorously the following spring. Instead, when harvesting cut whole spears from the *outside* of the clump, snipping them an inch or two above the ground level. The tiny sprouts in the center of the plant must be preserved for a continual supply of parsley. Biennial parsley is ready to be cut as soon as it is three to four inches tall. Save the stems for soup stocks if you aren't using them fresh. (I put mine in a freezer bag and add carrot peelings, celery tops, onion skins and the like for a soup stock.)

Curly Parsley is very hardy and may be clipped and used well into winter, even when the leaves have frozen. The second year plants seem to have more finely divided leaves and a grassier flavor. These leaves, of course, can also be used, but starting a new plant(s) every year is far better and more flavorful.

It is not recommended to shear a parsley plant when fully grown as the flowering and seeding is usually deterred in its second year. This full shearing will do much harm to future cropping. At the end of the growing season, if you do not wish to repot your parsley to bring indoors, you can winter them in a greenhouse. The other alternative is to leave them in the garden over the winter with some mulch applied. This will give them a sufficient start in the spring to produce their flowers and seeds in their second and final year.

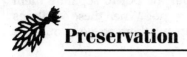 **Preservation**

When harvesting parsley for preserving, clip and gather stems from the outer portions of the plant on a sunny morning soon after the dew has disappeared. Rinse off any dirt, remove dead leaves and pat the sprigs dry on a paper towel.

While the leaves of most culinary herbs can be successfully dried for later use, I do not recommend this type of preservation for parsley because so little flavor is retained in the dried leaves. If you want to try drying parsley, however, use the Italian, flat-leaf variety. Dry it quickly on paper in a shady place as the leaves turn dark very easily.

Since delicate-tasting and tender-leaved herbs like the parsley, basil, and chives lose flavor in the drying process, they are better preserved by freezing. This can be done easily and quickly with wonderfully flavorful results. Some people blanche the leaves first in boiling water for a few minutes, then plunge in ice-cold water before freezing. This blanching will stop the enzyme process which can deteriorate the flavor and color. My method, however, is to simply wrap whole or chopped parsley and freeze in small vapor-proof bags. I remove as much air from the bag as possible to slow any deterioration. Though this parsley may wilt when frozen, the stems and leaves will retain most of their fresh flavor for up to one year in the freezer. When thawing, discard any leftover leaves that may warm up because they do not refreeze well. I always freeze my parsley whole and chop it when ready to use it. In this way the Vitamins are retained.

Parsley is so easy to grow, indoors or outside, or to purchase the year around, I don't preserve it very often. It is convenient, however, to have it in the freezer, close at hand.

🌿 Propagation

Unfortunately, parsley has a reputation for being difficult to grow from seed, mostly because it takes four weeks to germinate. Parsley's slow germination has stimulated some fanciful theories: "that it goes to the devil and back seven times before it sprouts," and "that a pregnant woman planting it speeds germination."

For spring sowing, soak seeds in tepid water for 24 hours before planting to speed germination. However, since soaking the seeds may cause them to stick together and make them difficult to sow, some gardeners have tried mixing the soaked seeds with sand or dry coffee grounds to keep them separated. Another method is to sow the seeds in a shallow trench and then pour scalding water down the row.

The soil should be 50° F. before planting the seeds in the spring, and for good results, parsley should always be sown thinly. Plant seeds one quarter inch deep and cover lightly with soil. Sow in rows one foot apart. Seeds must not be allowed to dry out. The principal sowing of parsley outdoors may be made in March for the summer and June for the winter. If one sowing is made, this should be done in May. In areas where summer temperatures are over 90° F. for prolonged periods, sow seeds in the fall. With the aid of a cloche or two (little caps) it is possible to have plenty of parsley all the year round outside. Thinning the individual plants to three inches apart and then to six inches should be done early to prevent them from crowding one another. This was described in the Planting & Care Requirements section.

Buying plants from a nursery is the way many busy gardeners, including myself, get parsley plants. Pot grown transplants tend to give you a more compact and vigorous leafy plant. Put these in a permanent plot or border in order to always have a good supply. By planting one parsley in each of two years and allowing each to go to seed in their second and final year, they will reseed and keep your parsley supply abundant.

ᵐ᷅♦ Culinary Uses

Parsley has a reputation as a 'companionable' herb in the kitchen because it lends subtlety to many of the stronger herbs and enhances the milder ones. It has a clean and delicate taste and a history of being appreciated. Parsley works with most foods except sweets and strengthens other flavors of cooked foods. To increase potency, use stems as well as the leaves. Store fresh cut parsley stems in a glass of water in the refrigerator, loosely covered with a plastic bag, or in a tightly sealed container. If stored in water, the water should be changed daily. This will stay fresh for about one week.

Parsley fills the role of an under-study in a play; it can play any part in case another herb is not available. Not a bad status! It reminds me of when I played softball for ten years, and was usually the 'utility' player. I could play any of the 10 positions when needed. (Not extremely well, of course, but I could play them all.) Parsley fills this role in the kitchen and because it is available year-round from the garden or the market it ends up on our table frequently.

Sometimes parsley is the only fresh herb at hand and it gives a dish that essential "fresh and alive" flavor and texture. It also reawakens dried herbs such as basil, tarragon, oregano, thyme, and marjoram. Simply mix the dried herbs called for in a recipe with a generous amount of freshly chopped parsley. Parsley can also be substituted for basil in a *pesto* in the winter. I use it in combination with several other herbs (cilantro and arugula, for instance) for *pestos*, as well.

France, specifically Burgundy, features parsley with ham in aspic; with garlic, butter, and escargots; and as *persillade*, a fine mince of garlic and parsley added at the last moment of cooking to sáutes, grilled meats, and poultry. The French also combine parsley with tarragon, chervil, and chives in their *fines herbes* mixture. This is used for seasoning egg and fish dishes, as well as in *bouquet garni*, a collection of various herbs (usually thyme, bay, and marjoram) tied up with string or in cheesecloth and used in cooking, stews, poultry, and fish. *Court bouillon* (a savory wine-and-herb broth used to poach fish and chicken) and homemade chicken broth are both incomplete without a handful of parsley.

The Belgians and Swiss are fond of fondue with deep-fried parsley on the side. The Japanese also deep-fry parsley in *tempura* batter. The Mexicans and Spaniards use parsley as the prime ingredient in *salsa verde,* and the English make parsley jelly.

Chimichurri, a dark-green, garlicky vinegar sauce loaded with parsley and other herbs, is a favorite in Mexican cooking. A similar sauce called *salmorejo,* smothered over grilled fish is favored in the Canary Islands. This is made by grinding dried oregano, garlic, lime juice, olive oil, and lots of fresh parsley into a thick green paste.

Chopped fresh parsley leaves can be a garnish or ingredient for soup, in meat loaf, stews and casseroles, or in omelets, poultry, stuffing and a sauce for fish stews and green salads. It goes well with rice, barley, *Tabbouleh* salad, or pasta dishes, especially when garlic predominates. Enhance peas, carrots, green beans or mashed potatoes with lots of minced parsley and green onions, butter, and fresh lemon juice. For a salad dressing, mix a generous amount of chopped parsley with sour cream, cream cheese or mayonnaise. As a vinegar, use with sage, shallots and red wine vinegar. I have tried parsley briefly deep fried as a side dish with fish and it's very flavorful.

Like mint, parsley is more generally used for garnishing and for flavoring. It is, however, a useful adjunct to any salad, providing it's used sparingly. Do not tear or cut parsley until you are actually ready to use it. When you cut into a food rich in Vitamin C, its cells release an enzyme called ascorbic acid oxidase. This enzyme destroys Vitamin C and reduces the nutritional value of the food.

The parsley root may also be cooked as a vegetable. I usually do this in the second year after the plant has gone to seed. The roots are quite tender and tasty.

Medicinal Uses

Parsley is controversial as a medicinal herb. Some dismiss it as "essentially worthless," while others say "it is a major medicinal plant." Parsley root, leaves, and fruit (seeds) all contain the volatile oil, but it is most concentrated in the seeds.

Medicinal uses of parsley are ancient and numerous since the plant is a rich source of Vitamins A and C, calcium, niacin, and, riboflavin. It also has other properties.

Parsley inhibits the secretion of histamine, a chemical the body produces that triggers allergy symptoms. It's apparently an antihistamine that might help those with hay fever or hives. A hot parsley tea has been used as a tonic for rheumatism and a diuretic when made from the seeds. *This 'prescription', however, can be hazardous to pregnant women.*

An infusion of tea made with stems and leaves drunk alone or combined with other herbs has long been a tonic to promote health in general and for constipation, specifically. Crushed leaves steeped in boiling water for a compress has been used successfully for sprains.

Prolonged handling of parsley plants may cause contact dermatitis (itching, burning, stinging, reddened or blistered skin), and can make the skin very sensitive to sunlight. This generally occurs with food workers who are handling parsley in large quantities without wearing gloves. There have been no reports of this dermatitis in people who eat parsley as a vegetable.

❓ Other Uses

Because of its chlorophyll content, parsley is chewed to sweeten the breath. When you find it on your dinner plate, be sure to eat it as a dessert.

Parsley oil is used in cosmetics, shampoos, perfumes, soaps, creams, and skin lotions. For cosmetic uses, it makes a good face pack for oily skin, and is a conditioner for dry, sensitive skin. It also adds shine and conditions dark hair in a rinse, and fades freckles when used as a skin lotion. (If I was fortunate enough to have freckles, I wouldn't want to fade them.) An infusion of parsley leaves is soothing and cleansing when added to your bath water.

 # Recipes

Blender Drink

Put three cups **tomato juice** in blender and add a handful of fresh **parsley leaves,** some **celery tops,** a few **mint sprigs**, juice of a **lemon** and a sprinkle of **cayenne**. Blend until well mixed and serve in a tall glass with ice, a lemon wedge, and sprig of parsley.

This healthful and refreshing tonic makes a great way to start the day or provide a revitalizing afternoon drink. (By the way, eat the garnish, too!)

Tartar Sauce

Combine one cup **mayonnaise,** two tablespoons chopped **parsley,** one tablespoon each of chopped **chives, tarragon, and chervil.** Add one teaspoon **onion,** one tablespoon **capers,** and one small **sour pickle.** Puree well in blender or food processor and add a little minced **garlic** if you prefer. Makes 1-1/4 cups.

A portion of the mayonnaise may be replaced with plain yogurt. Try this on fresh asparagus or green beans. This is such a fresh-tasting and unique sauce, you will never want to buy the stuff in a jar again! This keeps for weeks in the refrigerator.

Parsley Sauce

Puree in a blender, a large handful of **parsley** with one to two cloves of **garlic, olive oil**, and **Ricotta Cheese** to make a smooth paste. Adjust amounts as you blend according to the taste you desire. Good on cold beef, shellfish, and pasta.

Parsley Italian Dressing

Mix the following ingredients in a cruet or blender and refrigerate. One quarter cup each of **wine vinegar** and **olive oil**; one half cup **sunflower or canola oil**; one tablespoon each minced **parsley and minced onion**; one half teaspoon minced **sweet red pepper**; one teaspoon **lemon juice**; one half teaspoon **paprika**; one-quarter teaspoon ground **black or white pepper** and one clove minced **garlic**.

This is a particularly fresh dressing for a Mesculn (French baby greens) salad. It keeps well in the refrigerator for several days, but needs to be warmed a bit when taken out because the olive oil solidifies.

Parsley & Egg Sauce

Melt two tablespoons **butter** in a saucepan and stir in one and one half tablespoon **flour**. Cook for one to two minutes over medium heat. Pour in one quarter cup of heated **stock** and stir until blended, allowing to simmer for three minutes. Stir in one quarter cup **light cream** and add **salt and pepper** to taste. When smooth and well seasoned, stir in three or more tablespoons chopped **parsley** and two chopped **hard-boiled eggs**.

When using chicken stock, this sauce is great with pasta. If made with fish stock, serve with white fish, haddock or cod.

Egg Blend

Mix together one tablespoon **parsley,** one teaspoon each of **basil, chervil, chives, marjoram** and **tarragon.** Makes about three tablespoons. Use sprinkled on scrambled eggs or omeletes at the end of the cooking time.

Gourmet Parsley and Brown Rice Salad

Cook two cups of short grain **brown rice** in three cups of **water** for 35 minutes and cool. Make a dressing by combining one half cup each of **fresh lemon juice** and **olive oil,** three large cloves of minced **garlic,** one tablespoon of **honey,** and one teaspoon of **salt.** Mix well and pour three quarters of the dressing over the cooled rice. Combine one bunch of **scallions,** chopped, one half cup of chopped **parsley,** two tablespoons of chopped fresh **oregano or mint,** one cup toasted **almonds,** slivered, and a little **salt and pepper** to taste. Add this combined mixture carefully to the rice and remaining dressing, tossing lightly. This salad serves six to eight.

For a different taste in this salad, try adding two cups of **red or green seedless grapes,** halved, and/or one cup of canned **garbanzo beans,** drained. This recipe is very high in nutrition and satisfying while low in calories, fat and cholesterol.

French Mustard Slices for French Bread

Combine one half cup soft **butter or margarine,** one quarter cup snipped **parsley,** two tablespoons each of chopped **green onion** and prepared **mustard,** one tablespoon **toasted sesame seeds,** and one teaspoon **lemon juice.** Blend well and spread mixture on both sides of sliced French bread. Wrap loosely in foil and heat at 375° F. for 10-15 minutes.

Other Notes

Parsley is unusually rich in vitamins A, B, C and E as well as iron, chlorophyll and potassium. This is the reason why I add handfuls of it to blender drinks and other dishes. One half cup of chopped fresh parsley has only ten calories and provides .7 grams of protein, only a trace of fat, 2.1 grams of carbohydrates, 39 mg. calcium, 1.9 mg. iron, 27 mg. vitamin C (45% needed by a healthy adult each day) and 1560 IU vitamin A.

Parsley is useful as a cooking aid for reducing the cooking odors of strong vegetables such as onions, turnips or cabbages.

In the garden, parsley has been noted to aid growth of tomatoes and roses when planted nearby. This herb will repel asparagus beetles in a vegetable garden.

Parsley in floral arrangements helps keep the water fresh and can be used as the border in a tussie-mussie. Dried leaves and stems can be boiled to make a yellow-green dye.

This herb has been used to attract rabbits and hares, but to repel head lice.(I suppose we should sprinkle parsley around near Easter to attract Peter Rabbit. I don't know why else we would want to attract rabbits — especially to my garden.)

Because parsley seems so common, many people ignore it when shopping or planting their garden. I hope you will now give it the attention and place of honor it deserves on your table.

Rosemary

*The Grande Dame
of the Garden*

Rosemary

A symbol of love, friendship and remembrance, rosemary is still used popularly in wedding bouquets. It's said that it grows well where the 'mistress is the master.' The name rosemary comes from the Latin 'ros', meaning 'dew', and 'maris', the sea. This name probably was derived because the rosemary is so closely identified with the Mediterranean Sea and its surrounding areas. It is sometimes called rosemarine, *incensier* (French), or healing incense.

With rosemary as the Grande Dame in my herb garden, it makes the following axiom evermore true. "If you have your herb garden within ten yards of your kitchen, you'll use the herbs regularly. If it's twenty yards away, you'll use herbs once in a while. If it's more than twenty yards, you will probably just tell people that you have an herb garden." Plant your herb garden as close to the kitchen as you can, and you must include rosemary, so you will harvest it regularly.

🔬 Botanical Name

Rosemary — <u>*Rosmarinus officinalis*</u> — is sometimes known commonly as Polar Plant or Compass Weed, or Rosemarine. This plant has a variety of cultivars, and to many cooks, is one of the two best rosemary flavors for cooking.

Golden Rain Rosemary — <u>*Rosmarinus officinalis*</u> cv. *'Joyce De Baggio'* — is a tender perennial, bushy and compact with lovely dark blue flowers. Its golden leaves with green centers make this an unusual variety. It grows to five feet and can be used as a 'standard' for training. Its hardiness is to 20° F. with good winter protection. This is the other 'best flavor' for cooking that I have found. It is, however, difficult to grow in Western Washington.

Prostrate Rosemary — <u>*R. officinalis Prostratus*</u> — is a low-growing tender variety that makes a good ground cover, growing from 10-20 inches tall and spreading easily. This variety grows beautifully in rock gardens or hanging baskets. Its deep blue flowers bloom almost continuously.

Prostrate Rosemary — <u>*R. officinalis*</u> *'Prostratus'* cultivars: *'Santa Barbara'*, *'Lockwood de Forest'*, *'Ken Taylor'*, *'Huntington Carpet'* and others. These varieties have short, narrow green leaves with arching character. They are wonderful as ground covers or as hanging potted plants. The stems will root where they touch if laid in soil. The pale blue flowers bloom most of the year under the right climactic conditions. Their height ranges to three feet and most are hardy to 20° F. with some protection. *'Santa Barbara'* tends to get very woody but is semi-upright and fairly hardy. *'Huntington Carpet'* is a favorite in our area because its sky blue flowers are unusual.

Semi-Prostrate Rosemary — <u>*R. officinalis*</u> *'Severn Sea'* — is a hardy cultivar with mid-blue flowers and fine leaves on arching branches.

Trailing to Upright Rosemary — <u>*R. officinalis*</u> *'Miss Jessopp's Upright'* — is a hardy plant with pale blue flowers, green foliage and a tidy, growing habit. Because of its vertical growth, it is very useful for hedges.

Tuscan Rosemary — *R. officinalis* 'Tuscan Blue' — is an excellent garden variety which has broad, bright green leaves and lovely blue flowers. It's a rapid grower and gets quite tall. It's hardy to 5° F. with good protection. It's the second hardiest rosemary. 'Tuscan Blue' can grow to six feet or more. Although it's a vigorous grower it branches only moderately, even when pinch-pruned regularly. This is a good choice for a 'standard' or topiary in a pot or for an *espalier*.

Upright Rosemary — *R. officinalis* 'Benenden Blue' — is identical to varieties sold in the United States as *'Pine-scented.'* The very narrow leaves on twisting stems give a pleasant windswept look. With dark blue flowers this variety can grow to a height of five feet and is hardy to 20° F. with some winter protection. Its strong fragrance is rarely used in cooking, but is very fragrant in potpourri and other decorative uses.

White Rosemary —*R. officinalis* var. *albiflorus* — is an unusual white flowered rosemary. It is a dynamic and prolific bloomer that is also hardy to 20 F. In warmer zones this variety can become hedge-like, but in our area it seldom gets more than two feet tall.

Pink Rosemary — *R. officinalis* 'Majorca Pink' — has a pretty pink flower that blooms abundantly from September to December and its long stiff branches twist and cascade around the plant. It is half hardy with bright green leaves and a clean and fruity fragrance. It can grow to four feet and is winter hardy to 15° F. with protection. Its columnar growth makes it a good candidate for topiaries.

Arp Rosemary — *R. officinalis* 'Arp' — is cold hardy from 0° to -10° and will survive our Pacific Northwest winters if it is protected some. This is the hardiest of the rosemaries and since its introduction, now allows 60% of the nation's gardeners a chance to grow rosemary year around outdoors. This variety has pale green/gray leaves and blue flowers. It has become easier to find in local nurseries the past two years. With its compact, bushy foliage and clear blue flowers and green-gray leaves, it is my personal favorite.

Rosemary is a member of the *Labiatae* family which includes mints and many other herbs.

History

There are probably more legends, superstitions and historic uses of rosemary than any other herb. Remembrance, love, friendship, evil spirits, The Plague, Christ, passion, and many other words are associated with this famous herb.

Rosemary is native to the hills around the Mediterranean Sea, Spain and Portugal and has been introduced all over Europe. Because it stands for fidelity, friendship and loyalty, bridal wreaths were made from rosemary in the early Roman republic. Additionally, it was placed under nuptial mattresses to encourage faithfulness (probably to keep insects away as well). The Romans transplanted it to England's sea climate where it was mild enough to survive.

There are many romantic and folk myths surrounding rosemary. An old story says that the rosemary flower was originally white, but when the Virgin Mary laid her cloak of blue on the shrub on her flight to Egypt the flowers turned the color of the cloak. There is a lovely poem, *Ballad of the Rosemary*, written by Phyllis McGinley I recently ran across in a book called "A Wreath of Christmas Legends" which expands on this story of Mary and the rosemary bush. Since the Babe's swaddling cloths were also dried on the bushes and absorbed a wonderful aroma, fragrant rosemary baby linens were used by mothers during the Middle Ages to suppress bad dreams for their babes. Another non-Biblical myth revealed that rosemary would not grow more than six feet high in 33 years so as not to stand taller than Jesus Christ. Because of these legends and the fact that many rosemary plants bloom in early January during Epiphany, it is considered a highly favored Christmas green. Bound in garlands with bay, holly, mistletoe, and ivy, it was used to decorate hut and hall for the long Christmas revels.

People in ancient times used rosemary leaves to wrap their meats to keep them from spoiling. The antioxidant chemicals in rosemary act as preservatives to meats, even those with fat on them. Today we use BHA and BHT for chemical preservation, but the rosemary plant has been just as effective for many years.

This herb was used as a love charm in the Middle Ages. A young person would tap another with a rosemary sprig in bloom. This would supposedly make the selected person fall in love with them.

During the Middle Ages and Renaissance periods, every garden had at least one rosemary bush and it was often pruned into topiary (fanciful animal or symmetrical) shapes. Also around this time, rosemary was thought to ward off demons and to prevent bad dreams if a sprig was tucked under a pillow. We still make sleep pillows today with rosemary as one of the ingredients. It was believed that rosemary branches could even ward off witches when planted around one's dwelling, and would keep away the black death — The Plague — when burned in the homes of 14th and 15th century persons believing in this protection.

Greek students wore rosemary in their hair to help quicken the mind and improve the memory. During particularly difficult examinations, they would wear a whole wreath of rosemary so they had better recall. Rosemary has had a long reputation for improving memory.

This multitudinous herb was burned in sick chambers to purify the air, and branches were strewn in law courts as a protection from 'jail fever' or typhus. It was carried in neck pouches during The Plague to be sniffed when traveling through suspicious areas. During World War II, French nurses mixed rosemary leaves with juniper berries as an antiseptic in the hospital rooms. Even some early toothpastes were made with rosemary oils.

In some Mediterranean villages, bed linens were spread over rosemary bushes to dry so that the sun would extract the moth-repellant aroma. The aromatic wood of rosemary was sometimes used to make intricate inlaid boxes. When the box was opened and the recipient inhaled the aroma, it was believed to ensure that person a long and successful life.

Wealthy landowners in the 16th century scented their homes with rosemary incense. In these same times, however, if rosemary was planted around a home, it was a significant sign that the household was ruled by a woman. Men would tear these plants from the soil to show who was really boss in that abode.

The essential oil of rosemary was discovered early and found to have many uses in both the perfumery and medicinal industries. Rosemary oil has, in fact, been found to have antibacterial effects. It could have had some affect on the Black Plague after all.

Queen Isabella, of Hungary, credited rosemary with her regained youth and health. She drank a rosemary tea daily following a recipe that was given her by a hermit, and her gout improved greatly.

Myth and legend, fact and fancy. Rosemary is all of these.

 ## TYPE: Perennial *(semi-hardy)*

This aromatic evergreen shrub is mostly hardy, but some varieties are treated as tender perennial plants. In our area, you must bring them indoors during the coldest months of November, December, January and February. I plant my hardiest varieties (such as Arp) in containers for spring, summer and fall and then sink them in the ground for the winter months where they have a less likely chance of freezing.

Rosemary should not be considered totally hardy in the ground over a ten-year period in our USDA zone 8. We nearly always have a severe winter that kills them, even with good protection.

In Southern California and Nevada where I recently visited, I was pleasantly surprised to see the many rosemary bushes and hedges that grow wild along road sides and near city streets. These bushes were three to four feet across and nearly four feet tall. Some varieties were climbing fences and mingling along retaining walls. I really envy the people in those areas who can simply go out and pick long stems of rosemary branches whenever the desire for that lovely flavor or fragrance comes upon them. I've heard them say in those areas that rosemary 'grows like a weed' and you 'should whack it back' to keep it under control. Meanwhile I tend my little rosemary plants to keep them producing well, and bring those in that can't tolerate the cold winter months. No matter how much love and care I give to my rosemary plants, I will never have a bush as large and dramatic as those southern specimens.

Description

There are many varieties of rosemary, from tall woody shrubs to bonsai-like plants to creeping ground covers. They are usually placed in one of three categories: trailing, creeping (or prostrate) or upright. Upright plants are usually hardier than prostrate varieties. *'Miss Jessopp's Upright,'* a trailing variety with upright growth as well, has green needles and prostrate curving branches that grow in interesting shapes. Rosemary usually matures to two to three feet, but can reach over six feet depending on climate and variety. If temperatures in your area drop below 10° F., rosemary can be grown as a potted plant for summers outside and then wintered indoors. Most varieties do need good winter protection.

This distinctive, perennial, evergreen shrub has ash-colored scaly bark. The leathery, green-gray needlelike leaves gives it an overall graying, green appearance. Small oil glands cover the surface of the leaves like tiny insect eggs, but can't be seen with the naked eye. The squarish stems generally turn woody from the second year onward. When these dried stems are stripped of leaves they can be burned on a fire or in a barbecue for the aroma and flavor they impart. The seeds are very tiny, tan and oily.

Rosemary has cultivars of different hardiness and flower color. The varieties with small blue flowers are especially attractive to bees. Flowers bloom in shades of violet, blue, pink and white and will appear in the late winter, early spring, and late spring on most prostrate varieties, but some will blossom off and on throughout the year. Older plants with woodier stems tend to produce more flowers, and these are delicately shaped along the stems of the plant. The usual pale purplish-blue flowers are tiny, tubular and grow in spikes.There are usually just a few flowers on the plant at one time. Although a well-grown plant will bloom heavily in the cool weather of late winter and spring.

The fragrance of rosemary on the rocky hillsides of the Mediterranean is so strong that during the harvest season when the wind is just right, it can be smelled as much as twenty miles at sea. This must be a wonderfully pleasant experience for the mariners in the area.

The sweet-smelling leaves of rosemary have an aroma similar to pungent pine needles, and the whole plant has the same pleasant scent. A highly redolent plant, it has a refreshing fragrance of sea coast, pine, fir, and balsam and, therefore, is used extensively for *potpourri* and other decorative uses. Some people have said that the rosemary bush reminds them of turpentine. Indeed, there are some chemical constituents in common. The rosemary's essential oil is actually made up of almost three dozen compounds, many of these with a camphor-like scent. Different cultivars have similar but diverse aromas and flavors, as well as physical characteristics (leaf size, flower color, cold-hardiness), but most are good in culinary dishes.

Rosemary has an assertive, spicy flavor that is delicious with lamb, chicken and other meats and stuffing. Strong components of tannin and camphor tend to make it moderately bitter and peppery. For some individuals, rosemary flavor is an acquired taste, and then again, some never acquire a taste for it. See the Culinary Uses and Recipe sections for a collection of ideas in using rosemary in your kitchen.

 Planting & Care Requirements

Rosemary makes a lovely companion planting to lavender and assorted artemisia like Silver King or Silver Mound. I also like it with a plant commonly called Dusty Miller. These make a striking combination of sights for the eyes as well as scents for the nose. The trailing varieties work well as ground covers or for hanging on fences or garden walls. Rosemary is so bold and graceful it can stand alone in a garden. It can also be used with perennials in a larger landscape or as a border plant.

The dark green to gray-green of the rosemary shrub blends well with bright colors as well. Plant near colorful yellow marigolds or calendulas and bright red verbena for a very pleasing contrast of summer color. I recently planted some at the base of climbing roses for an exceptional effect.

Rosemary prefers a garden or deck location with full sun, but will tolerate partial shade. Without full sun, however, it is unlikely to bloom. These plants do like a lot of heat.

When planting in the garden, allow up to four feet per plant so that they have plenty of root space and air circulation for the branches even though they might not get that large for five to six years. Rosemary needs a very well-drained soil that is limed (alkaline, pH 6.0 to 7.5.) Although they have been known to do well in soil quite acid with a pH 4.9 to quite alkaline soil of pH 8.7, these are not optimum balances. Use a little limestone, crushed egg shells, or wood ash to keep the soil alkaline. If your soil is very sandy or heavy clay, add large amounts of humus, peat moss, compost, manure or other organic matter. In amending the soil in this way, you may need as much as five inches of matter added to create a good balance.

Plants in the ground need only one fertilization of all-purpose fertilizer in the spring to keep them healthy and productive. You may wish to fertilize with 10-10-10 liquid fertilizer at half strength once a month if your soil nutrients are not sufficient. If lanky growth develops because of your fertilization schedule, judicious pruning and pinching can keep it in check.

When a rosemary plant gets too dry, the leaves become more gray-looking and the leaf tips point upward rather than close to the stems. New growth will wilt if water is not given at this time, especially in the heat of summer. Less water is needed in the fall and winter when cloudy days are persistent. For a 'drought tolerant plant,' rosemary seems uncommonly needful of water when it is actively growing.

If the tops of the rosemary plant become woody, they can be trimmed. Cut a portion of each stem and then water the plant using a liquid fertilizer. New shoots should appear within a couple of weeks.

Rosemary will make a beautifully large potted plant. Use a two-gallon tub or basket to support a large, vigorously growing plant. Sink it in outdoor soil in summer, but return it to a green house or indoors during the winter. For a potted rosemary, fertilize every two weeks as above during the summer months.

When a plant is root-bound or needs fertilizer, the rosemary will have yellowing leaves around the base. After checking the root system, if it is root-bound, repot it into a container that is three or four inches larger. Cut about one third of the roots from the bottom of the ball with a sharp, clean knife. Make three vertical scoring slits along the root ball before replacing in the new moist soil. Clay pots should be thoroughly dampened before soil is added so that the pot doesn't absorb the moisture from the plant soil.

Rosemary is really a drought-tolerant plant because its native environs is the rocky, dry soil of the Mediterranean. Soil that is too wet around the roots, especially, will inhibit its growth and can subject the plant to root rot. *Do not over-water this drought tolerant plant.* But do watch that an actively growing plant gets enough water to sustain its growth.

If the leaf tips are browning and the needles eventually turn brown and die, the plant roots are dying from too much water. To save a plant in this condition, remove from the pot, cut off any browned dead roots, replace the soil with fresh dry potting soil, and replant the bush.

When this yellowing condition exists and the plant is not root-bound, the problem is probably lack of nutrients, in which case a small amount of fertilizer should improve the condition.

Rosemary plants should not be transplanted into fresh soil medium in the fall when brought in for the winter. Even if the plant is root-bound, it is better to leave it in its summer pot. Fresh medium will absorb too much water and cause the roots to rot before they have a chance to extend down into the soil. It is much better to transplant into a larger pot in the spring when ready to place it again into your frost-free garden.

Indoors, keep rosemary in a cool but sunny place and water regularly, but sparingly. If the soil becomes completely dry, it will usually go into a rapid and irreversible decline. Water well when moderately dry. Be sure the pot has a drainage hole and sets on gravel in a dish so that the roots are not subjected to constant wetness. Include some compost and moss in your planting soil for absorption.

Trailing rosemary does very well in a hanging basket or traditional "strawberry jar" arrangement when placed in a sunny location. As a houseplant it prefers a small pot, just large enough for its roots because it likes being crowded or it will develop root rot. Good drainage in a porous soil (like cactus soil with perlite with one tablespoon of lime for each four cups potting soil) is good for these indoor plants. Mist the branches regularly and don't let the roots dry out. Indoor rosemary needs at least four hours of direct sunlight per day or twelve hours of strong artificial light, but will seldom reach more than two feet tall. Pinching the tips will encourage and promote a bushy growth and this will also control the size and shape of the plant.

When a rosemary plant completely outgrows the largest of pots, you can still salvage the plant by severe pruning and repotting. In late spring or early summer, prune away large amounts of the roots, foliage and stems. This will encourage new growth. Of course, you will want to use the foliage in your kitchen and save the stems, too, for use in the fireplace or barbecue. Vigorous new growth should have sufficient time to reproduce with lots of sun and heat the remaining months of the summer. When planting the rosemary outside again in the spring, be sure that any danger of frost has passed. Choose a cloudy, overcast day to transplant into your prepared garden. Weather too hot and that is sunny can cause the plants to wilt and dry out rapidly. Water with a fine mist and leave a slight depression around the base of the plant.

Because rosemary does not suffer from reflected heat, it is a good candidate for patios and terraces. It can be placed in pots very near walls or snuggled into corners for a private garden view.

'Arp,' a fairly hearty rosemary variety, should have some protection in the winter especially from cold winds. If left outdoors, mulch the roots well with fir or pine boughs or dry leaves for the winter if temperatures drop below 25° F. Using organic material like grass clippings or wet leaves as mulch may cause disease during wet weather. Other varieties of rosemary that are less hardy need further protection to prevent damage to the needles and the forming flower buds. Place a plastic sheet around the plant and tie with a twine. Leave the top portion open so that heat from winter's sun does not cook the plant and break its dormancy. Bob Lilly, my technical editor who lives on a houseboat, simply uses a bed sheet to protect his rosemary plants on the few days he has below freezing temperatures.

Pests and diseases are not a great problem with rosemary grown outdoors. Aphids, mealybugs, whiteflies and other pests more commonly bother this herb when it's indoors. Again, use of an insecticidal soap spray can be applied to control most pests. In very humid climates, some fungal diseases are present. Good air circulation around the plants is a big deterrent to this type of disease. Garden sulfur is a reliable cure for mildew.

Harvesting

Rosemary twigs and leaves can be harvested at any time once the plant has become established. Even in the winter, a garden rosemary may have the stem tips picked for use in the kitchen. However, you must be careful not to pick full stems that may affect the ability of new growth.

Picking the rosemary sprigs in the morning when the dew is off the needles (leaves) will produce a more aromatic and tasty harvest. This is the same rule for harvesting all of the herbs in this book. The essential oils are at their highest peak at that time. The most important aspect of harvesting rosemary *is to pick no more than 20% of a plant at a time or it will slow down and sometimes stop production*. For small amounts of rosemary you may pinch off the tips of several branches one or two inches. This will also encourage continuing growth. You may also take entire sprigs to use for stuffing or other purposes if you follow the 20% rule. New growth will not appear on the stems when the flowers are in bloom. Therefore, if you want continuing leaf growth, remove six to eight inches of the tip growth regularly. Rosemary should be harvested for preservation as the flowers appear. If harvesting for the flowers in the kitchen, cut the stems when flowers are in full bloom and keep the stems in water until ready to use. Pinch the flowers from the stems, rinse and pat them dry. The flavor of the flowers are much like the leaves of the plant but milder. See the Culinary Use section for further ideas.

 ## Preservation

Rosemary leaves should be dried quickly to preserve their oil and dark green color. If dried too slowly, the oil dissipates into the air rather than being captured in the leaves. The dark green color also will turn to more gray color if left too long to dry. Rosemary either dried or frozen retains its flavor and color. To freeze, rinse and dry whole fresh picked sprigs. Place in zip-type plastic freezer bags (these are not the thinner lunch bags) with all the air removed. You may use a straw to suck out any extra air. These stems can also be frozen in jars with tight fitting lids. Remove the leaves from the stems before using the rosemary. The frozen rosemary tends to be stronger in flavor than the fresh.

The tips and leaves may be dried for future use, but since the plant is evergreen, fresh tips are usually available if you are wintering your plant(s) indoors.

Dry the needles (leaves) whole on the stems to preserve the oils. This should be done before the plant flowers for the best results. Spread the cut stems on a screen and dry in a dark, well-ventilated place. Rosemary also dries well by hanging in bunches as described in the chapter on lavender. Be sure to swish the bunches in lukewarm water first to remove any dust or small bugs. Dry them where they will stay clean, or place a paper bag, with holes in it for moisture escape, around the bunch. Keep the leaves on the stems. When you remove the leaves from the stems for use, remember to save the stems to use in the fireplace for a pleasantly scented, winter evening. When rosemary is very dry, the needles tend to be sharp (much like pine needles) so you may wish to use gloves to remove the needles from the stems and to package them. The larger the needles, the longer they will retain their flavor when dried. Be careful, also, not to crush the leaves at this point. They should be stored as whole as possible and then crushed just before using.

 **Propagation**

Rosemary germinates very slowly from seed, and the germination rate is low and erratic because the seeds have little vigor. As few as 10 seeds in 100 will germinate. These seeds additionally need at least 70° F. and a constantly warm environment. *Rosmarinus officinalis* is the only variety that should be attempted from seed. Because packaged seeds are difficult to germinate, use fresh seeds, less than two weeks old. Seed them in the permanent garden location at least six inches apart, as they do not transplant well. Or you may sow the seeds indoors in spring and then transplant to the outdoor garden in summer. Rosemary plants grown from seeds are not as robust as those grown from cuttings or divisions of established plants. The stems are softer, branches weaker, and leaf color lacks the sheen and intensity of rosemary grown from cuttings.

It can take as long as three years to produce a sizable plant even from a nursery start. Cuttings, layering and divisions can all be used to propagate rosemary, but I prefer the cutting method. In August, clip a sprig of firm new growth three to four inches long, that is not woody, from the top of the plant. Strip the bottom one to one and one half inches of all leaves and dip this bare stem into a rooting hormone. Place the sprig in wet sand or starter soil about one inch deep, leaving only two inches of the twig above ground. Cover with a large jar for about two to three weeks until the plant has rooted. Water covered cuttings during dry spells. When new top growth appears, transplant the cuttings into individual pots filled with a good commercial potting soil, firming the soil around the roots. Keep these starts indoors in the winter. In the spring, check the root ball for new white roots. Plant entire root ball in the well-drained herb garden after danger of frost.

You may also take cuttings from a vigorous, healthy plant and place in a vase of water on the window sill to root. Change the water daily for a fresh oxygen supply. The rooting may take four or five weeks this way, where soil planting will take only about two weeks. Most cuttings will develop roots eventually. If using the water method, you need also to strip the lower leaves from one half of the cutting. Rooting hormone can again be used but isn't essential. I have found this an easy way to propagate the rosemary cultivars that I most enjoy. Transplant these cuttings when they are six to eight inches tall, and leave at least two to three feet between plants.

When planting into outdoor soil, dig a hole about the size of the root ball and set the plant in the hole with a slight twist to settle it into the soil. Spread the roots gently and plant only to the depth it was growing before. Don't pack the soil too tightly around the roots because it needs some air spaces.

For plant divisions, dig up a fairly young plant in the autumn or early spring. You must be very careful not to injure the root system. Divide carefully and replant two to three feet apart to encourage bushy growth.

To layer a mature rosemary plant, pin down the lowest, rambling, woody branches against the soil until roots form. This can take several weeks. Tug on the upper branch to see if it is firmly attached in the soil and then cut from the 'mother' plant and replant in another location.

When a rosemary plant finally takes hold and is wintered correctly, it can last for many generations. I hope to have one eventually six feet tall that I can pass on to my children. I hope you will, too.

▄▌▐● Culinary Uses

Rosemary, like most herbs in cooking, should enhance the dish's flavor, not overwhelm it. It is a seasoning that combines both strong and subtle qualities with a pungent, pine-like, bittersweet flavor and has a slightly ginger finale.

In Italy especially, rosemary is much revered as a culinary herb. Sometimes, butchers in northern Italy give a branch of rosemary or sage with the meat purchases. The British were introduced to rosemary by the Romans, and the Brits still love to flavor their food with it —especially grilled meat. They also continue to use it as a meat preservative.

When using rosemary in cooking, it is better to err on the side of moderation. This is a strongly pungent herb, with a little rosemary going a long way. Start with a small amount in a recipe and then increase it as your tastes dictate. As you grow to experience and appreciate rosemary's fine flavor, you may want to increase the amount (fresh or dried) in your recipes. One teaspoon of dried herb is equivalent to three teaspoons fresh.

It is best to use rosemary, sage or thyme individually or with milder herb combinations only. Complimentary herbs of chives, chervil, parsley, and bay are all good in recipes. Rosemary's taste is pungent and mint-like but a little sweeter than mint or these others.

This herb serves as a wonderful 'sweet enhancer.' Add rosemary to a fruit salad to make it seem sweeter without adding sugar. Use in cakes instead of cinnamon or allspice. Try it in jams, jellies, wine and fruit cups, especially citrus (orange). If you are lucky enough to have bee hives in your area around the rosemary, they make a wonderful rosemary honey. I can sometimes find this variety locally.

Oil of rosemary which is extracted from the leaves and flowers is used to flavor candy, baked goods and liqueurs. It is also used abundantly in the perfume industry.

Rosemary's robust character adds pizzazz to salad dressings, *bouquet garni,* and lentils. Other foods that are enhanced by its flavor are eggs, cheese, and cream sauces. You can substitute mint and ground ginger or sage for rosemary for a similar taste effect.

Gentle soups with potatoes and eggplant benefit from rosemary, as well as a fresh mushroom soup. Fresh or dried rosemary leaves in split-pea soup are a tasty winter treat, and they also go well with wine and garlic in soups and stews.

The flowers taste much like the foliage but are milder. These are used to garnish salads, beverages, and desserts as well as tea sandwiches and herb breads spread with cheese. Pound fresh flowers with sugar, mix with cream, and add to a fruit puree for a delightfully easy dessert. Use both flowers and leaves for garnishing and cooking.

Crystallizing the flowers for a garnish is easy and fun although it does take some patience. Wash and dry fresh flowers. Combine an egg white with a few drops of water and beat lightly. Brush the egg white mixture on a flower and then sprinkle superfine sugar over it. Place on waxed paper to dry. Store these dried candied flowers in an airtight container and they will keep for as long as a year.

Rosemary makes a wonderful full-flavored vinegar alone or with a combination of other herbs and spices. The flavor harmonizes with honey, marmalade, both orange and lemon preserves or butters, and mustard. Rosemary's pungent but sweet flavor blends especially well with both black and red raspberries, blueberries, currants, or boysenberries.

This is a great roasting herb because the flavor holds up well over fairly long cooking times. I also use it in baking and barbecuing. When grilling, add a handful of damp rosemary stems to the coals during the last five or ten minutes of cooking for a smoky rosemary flavor. Make a marinade of rosemary, red wine and olive oil to use on pork chops or lamb and then roast or grill the meat. It is also wonderful in stews of beef, pork or game. Fish, especially shellfish and trout, are genuinely delicious with this sweetly fragrant herb. Rosemary jelly with turkey on cold sandwiches is a popular after-Thanksgiving luncheon at our house. All kinds of beef, fish, fowl and stuffing, lamb, veal, pork and wild game benefit from this addition. A wonderful chicken recipe follows as well as my baste for the Thanksgiving turkey. Mince the leaves very finely when preparing a dish with rosemary as larger pieces can cause damage to esophagus or stomach linings.

Vegetables of all kinds are superb grilled or steamed with rosemary. My favorites are potatoes, asparagus, tomatoes, green beans, and zucchini squash. Rosemary is well-known as a flavor enhancer with spinach, peas, mushrooms, and earthy vegetables like turnips, broccoli and cabbage.

The fresh leaves have a more delicate taste than those that are dried. Dried leaves can be used to mix in ground meat for hamburger patties, or in tuna, pasta or potato salads to help preserve from food poisoning. (Although this is no substitute for proper refrigeration.)

Make a traditional dumpling or biscuit recipe and add one half teaspoon of dried, crushed rosemary. Add one tablespoon crushed rosemary for each loaf of baked bread. I recently received a bread-maker as a gift and my first loaf of white bread was made with crushed dried rosemary leaves. What a taste treat — and so easy to make! Rosemary butter is luscious on hot biscuits, giving a woodsy, earthy scent and taste.

Hot herbal teas, called tisane, can be easily made by combining two teaspoons of freshly cut rosemary (or one teaspoon dried) for each six ounce cup of tea. This tea is reminiscent of China Tea *(Camellia sinensis)* because of its astringency.

Make a wine/rosemary marinade by adding two thirds cup of rosemary sprigs to two cups dry red wine; cork and store in the dark for a week or so. I always keep this on hand to marinate pork, lamb, or beef. You may also simply add a sprig of fresh rosemary to a glass of white wine for a refreshingly piney, pungent drink. After absorbing the wine flavor, remove these sprigs and use on broiled fish, lamb, or poultry.

Rosemary is one of the better herbs to use if making herbed oil. Use a good quality olive oil such as Bertolli or a milder Safflower or Canola oil. Be sure the rosemary leaves are very dry when put in the oil. It will take two to three weeks to infuse the oil with the rosemary flavor. *Always remember to store the oil in the refrigerator to prevent botulism.*

Rosemary has so many uses in the kitchen, you can see why I never have enough in my garden to suit all of my needs. And wait until you read what it does for your health and beauty!

 # Medicinal Uses

Of all the herbs valued by the ancients for medicinal purposes, rosemary was perhaps the most versatile and beloved. You will note the host of uses below. As one of 130 odd herbs that are used in tea, it also has more uses than any other.

Because the healing properties of rosemary were discovered early, it traveled north across Europe and Britain with the Roman legions, becoming a salve for wounds in addition to a tea for indigestion. Remember Queen Isabella and her gout.

Externally, it can help wounds and soothe mouth infections, bruises, and sprains. Because it has antiseptic properties, it's helpful as a poultice for stings, bites, cuts and sores, and is used in liniments for aching muscles. The leaf is recognized as a stimulant for toning the cardio-vascular system by increasing blood supply where it is applied.

Rosemary is also used as an anti-spasmodic which will help relax the muscle lining of the digestive tract and helps aid in the digestion of fats. This action does not necessarily hold true with the muscle lining of the uterus, however. In fact it can cause stimulation of the organ and bring on a menstrual period.

Rosemary tea, known as tisane, is an infusion made from the fresh leaves and drunk for its mildly medicinal affect. An infusion is a useful tonic for asthma, insomnia, anxiety, anemia, depression, and nervous migraine. Tea of this antiseptic herb is also used for a soothing gargle, sore throat, or bad breath. Hot rosemary tea is used for stimulating circulation and for colds, nasal and chest congestion, influenza symptoms, and allergies. An aromatic infusion is also used to settle the stomach or as a diuretic tonic. For these internal uses, steep one teaspoon of fresh crushed herb in one cup of boiled water for 10-15 minutes. You can drink this amount safely three times a day. More than this amount could irritate the stomach. Two ounces of infused tea at a time is a good remedy for gas, colic, indigestion and fever. This great tea at the end of a harried day certainly calms my body and mind. I hope you will try it, too.

A tincture of rosemary can also be taken internally for aches and pains. The mixture is made by infusing flowering tips in alcohol for a month and then straining. Use just one teaspoon of this mixture per day.

The French term for rosemary, *incensier*, comes from its use as incense in church ceremonies. This has been used not only for its penetrating scent but also because of its reputation to ward off evil spirits. It additionally has a calming effect on the parishioners.

Although rosemary is safe in its natural state, even small amounts of rosemary oil (which is very concentrated) may cause stomach, kidney or intestinal irritation. Like many other herbs, however, it is very safe if used in moderate amounts. *Pregnant women or nursing mothers should not use the preparations internally without checking first with a physician.*

? Other Uses

The essence of rosemary is so unique and long lasting; it is used extensively in the perfume industry. Soaps, creams, lotions, deodorants, toilet water and hair tonics are all made from rosemary oil. It can, however, cause contact dermatitis with itching, burning or reddening of the skin in very sensitive people.

Rosemary oil has been used commercially as well as in embalming fluids. The more ordinary uses in a modern household, however, are in bath bags, sleep pillows (perhaps to ward off nightmares) and for sachets and *potpourris*. The flowers and foliage of this herb give a wonderful woodsy or earthy scent to *potpourri* whether used alone or with thyme, sage or Sweet Woodruff.

In a hot herbal rosemary bath, you can expect rejuvenation of a sluggish body because the volatile oils in rosemary stimulate blood circulation. This invigorating action especially boosts circulation and deep cleansing when the rosemary bags are used to scrub the skin, as well as steep in the bath water. See some good recipes for bath bags in the next section. For a fragrant and revitalizing bath, try rosemary leaves mixed with lavender flowers, rose petals and the zest from a tangerine (the orange part without the pith). Try rosemary, too, as a foot bath, alone or with mint. It really does refresh tired feet.

Also cosmetically, rosemary is wonderful along with sage as a hair rinse for dark hair. It strengthens and deepens the color as well as imparting a lovely fragrance, much as Lemon Balm does for blonde hair.

Because rosemary oil contains astringent compounds called tannin, it is used in facial cosmetics. A good cleansing facial steam can be achieved by using a strong infusion of rosemary tea. Allow it to cool sufficiently, then place your face over the pan with a towel over your head for ten minutes. This gives a good cleansing and tightening action to the pores and should be followed by a cool water rinse and pat dry.

For an herbal cleansing oil, place sprigs of rosemary leaves in a small jar with warmed safflower or sunflower oil and use for dry skin. Another rosemary skin care suggestion is to boil a handful of rosemary leaves and flowers in one half pint of water for five minutes. Cool the solution, strain and use in a light film as freshener. Allow to dry completely and apply moisturizer.

Hungarian women are noted for their complexions. The legend of the Hungarian Queen and her secret Budapest Water follows. Queen Elizabeth of Hungary, a famous beauty, was so attractive at the age of 70 that she inspired a young man of 26 with a 'burning passion.' Her secret recipe for a beauty bath:

> 4 oz. rosemary leaves, 1 cup mint leaves, 1 cup Lemon Balm, 3 cups rosewater, 1 pint alcohol, peel of one fresh lemon and one orange. Place all herbs and peels, dried (or double

amounts if fresh from your garden) into a large jar and pour the liquids over them. Let the mixture stand for a month in a warm place, then strain and filter. Budapest Water should be used at your own risk for attracting younger men.

If this seems like too much trouble to you, (it certainly does to me!) I simply place dried or fresh rosemary leaves (sometimes with other herbs) in a small square handkerchief, tie the four corners together with a long string and then hang it on the bath tub spout and let the warm water run over it while I fill the tub. This makes a great restorative herbal bath, and doesn't make me hungry like the basil bath. This is a much easier method for our busy lives. I'm just happy when I have time for a leisurely bath instead of a two minute shower.

In years past, rosemary was considered a love potion, but I am not sure whether you drank it, bathed in it, or gave it to your lover. This must be legend, as I haven't found any incredible amorous properties in my rosemary bushes.

Shakespearean bouquets or tussie-mussies, are still popularly created with rosemary along with other aromatic herbs for special events. Herbal weddings are becoming fashionable, and these tussie-mussies are very stylish.

Sprigs of this plant were placed in the hands of the deceased before burying. Whether this was to ward off evil spirits or used for the fragrance before embalming, I have not been able to determine.

Floral arrangements benefit from the addition of rosemary, especially if it is in bloom. I use it with pink and silver-tone flowers and herbs like carnations and lavender. Try making a moth bag with a mix of dried rosemary, mint, santolina, and mugwort in a firmly stitched, semi-porous bag. This really is a good moth repellent for your closets or drawers.

Rosemary leaves are popular in candle-making as they give the candle wax a dark olive green color as well as a pungent piny fragrance.

Recipes

There are so many wonderful recipes using rosemary, I have given you just a few of those that are our favorites. But as explained in the Culinary Section, the uses for this herb in cooking are almost unlimited. Rosemary is wonderful in herbed oils, marinades, butters, and vinegars. Also in a pesto, use the recipe for basil but substitute one third cup rosemary and one and one half cups of parsley or chervil.

Rosemary Butter

Soften one stick (one half cup) of **sweet, unsalted butter.** Add two **scallions,** finely chopped (white part only), two tablespoons finely chopped, fresh **rosemary leaves,** one quarter teaspoon fresh ground **pepper,** one teaspoon **lemon juice,** one half teaspoon **lemon zest** and a pinch of ground **cayenne pepper.** Mix thoroughly with the back of a wooden spoon or in a food processor. This can be frozen for several months.

Rosemary Potatoes

Scrub two large **baking potatoes.** Cut potatoes in half lengthwise and dip the cut edge in melted **butter** and then in a mixture of one half teaspoon crushed **dried rosemary,** one clove of **minced garlic,** and one quarter cup of **Parmesan cheese.** Bake potato halves cut side up at 350° F. until tender, about 30 minutes. (Or wrap in foil and cook on barbecue.) I sometimes slice the potatoes in half inch slices, dip and grill. For fewer calories, of course you may use margarine.

Rosemary Vinaigrette

Whisk together in a small bowl, three tablespoons fresh **lemon juice** (or herbal vinegar), two tablespoons **olive oil,** one teaspoon of **mustard** (I prefer Dijon), one clove of minced **garlic,** and one teaspoon of dried minced **rosemary** (one tablespoon if using fresh). Pour into a cruet and refrigerate.

This is a simple vinaigrette to use over pasta, steamed vegetables or green salad.

Rosemary Chicken

Rinse and dry one large **roasting (or fryer) chicken** with giblets removed. Stuff the chicken cavity with pieces of fresh **onion,** several whole garlic **cloves,** and eight to ten fresh **rosemary** sprigs. I sometimes place rosemary sprigs under the skin on the breast and between the wings and body for extra external flavoring. Rub chicken with **olive oil** and sprinkle with a little fresh **lemon juice or herbal vinegar.** Roast on a grill or in the oven until completely done (185° F. internal temperature). Let set for ten minutes before removing rosemary sprigs and then carving.

This is equally good with Cornish game hens, turkey or capon.

Rosemary-Butter Baste

Similar idea to the above. We use this every Thanksgiving and anytime I roast a whole turkey.

Heat one half cup each **dry white wine** and **butter** over low to medium heat until butter is melted. Add one teaspoon **dried minced rosemary** (or one tablespoon fresh) and two tablespoons **catsup** for a rosy color. Add water to the pan below the roasting turkey to collect drippings and prevent pan from burning. Baste turkey every one half hour or so while it roasts. Skim fat and make a sauce of the rosemary baste with some water added.

Herb Garden Potpourri

2 cups thyme	1/4 cup tansy
1 cup rosemary	1/4 cup cloves
1/2 cup lavender	1/2 oz. orris root (fixative)
1 cup mint	few drops of essential oil

Two days ahead of time, sprinkle several drops of **essential oil** over the **orris root** in a small glass jar, cap it tightly and set aside. Essential oil of bayberry, patchouli, sandalwood, myrrh or frankincense are all excellent with this recipe. Lightly crush any **whole spices** with a mortar and pestle. Combine them with the **herbs** in a non-metallic bowl. Toss all the dried ingredients with your hands. Sprinkle on the oil and fixative mixture and mix well. Pour all this into a wide-mouthed jar with enough room to shake. Set in a warm, dark place and turn the jar over and shake it twice a week to blend the mixture well. In about a month, your *potpourri* should be mature with a well-blended fragrance.

You can use this mixture in an open bowl or capture it in securely stitched bags of a semi-porous material for drawers or closets.

Rosemary Christmas Potpourri

1 cup of bay leaves
4 rosemary sprigs 5-6" long
6 cinnamon sticks 3" long
6 cloves
Zest or rind of an orange or lemon

Place all ingredients in a pan with 4 cups of **water** and bring to a boil. With heat down, simmer on the stove. This makes a wonderful room fragrance while you are trimming your tree, wrapping gifts or baking cookies. It can be used several times.

Rosemary Massage Oil

Combine one quarter ounce of **rosemary oil** with eight ounces of warmed **olive oil**. Have your favorite partner rub it onto aching muscles. Use mint instead of rosemary for stimulating the muscles.

Rosemary Bath Rub

Simmer a large handful of fresh or **dried rosemary** in three cups of **water**. Add to one cup of oatmeal. Put in muslin bag with a drawstring top and use as a body scrubber in the bath.

✍️ Other Notes

Training rosemary on standards in various shapes can be easily done. You can design these for your outdoor garden or enjoy them indoors. The training takes patience and care, but is by no means a task for experts only. Rosemary is a good candidate for this art form because it is a fast growing woody shrub that produces many small sized leaves. When the standard has grown to three or four feet in height, the crown of small leaves atop the single trunk helps to create the impression of a real tree in miniature. Container growing of standards is preferable to growing them directly in the garden. Rosemary can also be grown into various shapes around wire and as topiaries.

Rosemary, like thyme, attracts and offers shelter to beneficial predator insects such as spiders and ground beetles. The lacewings and lady beetles also like the nectar and pollen of the rosemary flowers in addition to all of the aphids they devour.

Although it's not generally used for this purpose anymore, rosemary has been used as a dye for wool. It will turn the wool a yellow to green color, depending on the variety used.

Rosemary is very effective in keeping moths away from woolens. Try some dried rosemary sewn into interestingly shaped bags for your closets and drawers. It acts as a general insect repellent in the garden or indoors. A branch of fresh rosemary boughs placed in a room will scent the air. This herb has also been used to purify stale water.

Can you believe how many uses there are for rosemary! I'm sure that there are many that I have not yet discovered, and if I ever grow enough of this delicious and aromatic plant, I might be able to use more of it in experimentation.

Sweet Cicely

The Sugar-Saver Herb

Sweet Cicely

This wonderful herb is so overlooked by most gardeners that I felt I must include it in this book if for no other reason than to give it some well-deserved recognition! Most people reading this book are probably vaguely familiar with all other herbs I have listed from basil to thyme, but Sweet Cicely may be new to you. I hope it won't be a stranger in your garden for long.

Herb gardens are about peace, serenity and tranquility. A place of relaxation and beauty is especially created when Sweet Cicely grows in a shady corner. It is very comforting on a warm spring day to see this majestic herb with beautiful white flower sprays. When the licorice pods are green, the neighborhood children flock to the Sweet Cicely plant like bees to a honeycomb.

 ## Botanical Name

Sweet Cicely — *Myrrhis odorata* — is also known as British Myrrh, Anise, Anise Fern, Great Chervil, Sweet Chervil, Smooth Cicely, and Shepherd's Needle. The origin of the name is not as angelic as it sounds. The Greek word, *seseli*, refers to a genus of *Umbellifers* (carrot-like plants) which are also anise flavored. The generic name is derived from the Greek word meaning 'smelling of myrrh' and the Latin *odorus*, for 'fragrant'. This herb is very fragrant with a lovely perfume. This is not the plant, however, that produces anise seed. That plant is <u>*Pimpinella anisum*</u>, a hardy annual.

Sweet Cicely is a member of the <u>*Umbelliferae*</u> family which also includes parsley and carrots.

History

Sweet Cicely is native to Europe and is cultivated there extensively as well as in Asia where it has been used in cooking for centuries. Being naturalized in North America now, it grows in many areas of our country including grassy, woody and mountainous areas. Sweet Cicely has been in use since Roman times for cooking and medicinal purposes.

It sometimes has been compared historically with chervil as well as anise, but it really is a plant of its own. Myrrh oil was one of the three gifts given to the Christ Child by the Three Wise Men, and it has for centuries been considered a precious and expensive oil.

Before furniture polish was commercially made, Sweet Cicely was a popular plant to use for this purpose. The seeds were crushed and rubbed into the wood with a soft cloth to give it a fragrant smell as well as a protective finish. See a recipe for this in the Recipe section.

TYPE: Perennial *(hardy)*

Sweet Cicely is one of the hardiest perennial plants in this area. It is one of the first to arrive in the spring herb garden and one of the last plants to leave in the fall. It is also the first plant in my spring garden to attract the bees. As an herbaceous plant, it dies to the ground level each fall to return royally in the spring. I welcome it each year.

Description

Sweet Cicely is a very handsome plant and looks somewhat like a giant chervil plant while others think it similar to celery. Visitors to my garden sometimes even mistake it for a fern. Its flowers, stems, leaves, seeds and roots are all used in a variety of ways and all are edible. The feathery leaves have a sweet anise or licorice flavor. Along with this sugary sweet flavor, a myrrh-like scent permeates the air when even a light breeze blows. This pleasant scent has overtones of moss and woodlands and some think its essence is similar to lovage, very fresh and heady. It's considered a sugar-saver herb and sometimes lovingly referred to as the candy or licorice plant. This very aromatic two to five foot tall specimen has a princely grandeur in its slow growing manner.

The white flowers that appear in early summer are small and lacy, very light and delicate. These tiny flowers grow in clusters two inches across in compound umbels. Interestingly, the inner blooms are male while the outer blooms are bisexual. When in bloom, my Sweet Cicely reminds me of a small snowfall on a fern bed. Some people advise that these beautiful flower clusters should be cut off to retain maximum flavor in the leaves of the plant. One or two may be left to set seed. I have not found any diminishing of the oils in the leaves by leaving the flowers on, however.

The fruit or seeds are long and light green when young. They turn dark brown or black when ripe and lengthen to one inch. The neighbor children and I eat the seed pods when they are still green for a true licorice and nutty flavor treat.

The fernlike, lacy leaves are large and green with a fine down and spotted on the underside. They wrap around the stems rather than growing on just two sides. These light green leaves turn purple in the autumn. When exposed to sun over a long period, the leaves turn yellow to white and are not as attractive. This is the plant's way of saying that it prefers a shady to semi-shady habitat. The hollow stems make great straws for summer drinks as they impart a slight licorice flavor. I use them to drink my ice water when I'm out weeding the garden. Sweet Cicely has a thick taproot that is also edible but, of course, you have to dig up the plant to get it.

All parts of this extraordinary plant have been used in medicine as well as in cooking.

Planting & Care Requirements

Sweet Cicely is one of the easiest herbs to grow. It likes a humus soil, kept moist and a slight acidity of pH 5.5 to 6.5. This soil should contain some compost or manure but be well-drained. Because of its taproot, the soil needs to be well prepared by digging it deeply so the roots have a good chance for penetration. Heavy clay soil will need an amendment of organic material for proper drainage. The plant will adjust fairly easily to any kind of soil but does like some compost or manure additives.

Because the plant thrives in partial shade, it is a good choice for growing under trees and in stands. Try plantings nearby of hosta, polyganatum (Solomon's Seal,) smilacina (false Solomon's Seal) or astilbe, a lovely perennial plant with colorful plumage. Sweet Cicely also makes a wonderful semi-tall border along a fence line. It also looks attractive in the back of the garden until late autumn when the leaves start to turn brown. I usually cut mine back quite severely at that time.

This shade lover can be grown in all parts of the country, except with some difficulty in the Gulf areas and Florida. This hardy perennial needs a good, cold dormant season to complete its annual growth cycle.

Harvesting

Leaves can be picked any time during the growing season, from February until September, to flavor culinary dishes. One plant will harvest one half cup of seeds during one growing season and about four cups of leaves. The bottom outer leaves will yellow as new growth continues to appear in the center of the plant. The flowers and seeds can be harvested as needed for bouquets or for munching. Most gardeners prefer to pick the green immature seeds in midsummer to flavor herb mixtures and salads. The flowers can be harvested as they appear for use in floral bouquets or left on the plant to add a real touch of elegance.

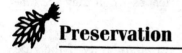

Preservation

The leaves can be dried for use in the late winter months when Sweet Cicely is in dormancy, but they do not retain nearly the scent as when fresh. A dried Sweet Cicely herbal tea is a great pick-me-up on cold winter mornings. Pick the newer, smaller leaves and dry quickly on trays. Place them whole in an air-tight jar. These dried leaves are good for *potpourri* and sachets as well.

The flower heads can be dried and used in flower arrangements in winter bouquets. The green immature seeds may be picked and pickled in a white wine vinegar. Ripe seeds (dark brown) can be harvested and dried for medicinal or culinary uses. The root can be dug up, cleaned, peeled and infused in wine or brandy.

Because fresh Sweet Cicely leaves are available from February through September (or the first frost), I do not preserve them very often. I do, however, like to keep one pint jar of dried leaves on hand for that mid-winter morning pick-me-up tea.

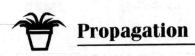

Propagation

Sweet Cicely can be propagated by two different methods; seeds and transplanting divisions. Seeds are best planted when they are fresh, using the current year's growth. To retain the germination power of the seeds, place new seeds in a plastic bag with moist peat moss and refrigerate for several weeks before planting them in small pots. If planting directly in the garden in the fall, plant about one quarter inch deep. These will germinate easily after a mysterious series of freezing and thawing. The seeds need several months of cold winter temperature which is why they do not grow well in southern states. The seeds are slow to germinate and grow because of these climactic needs. Thin the seedlings to two feet apart when they reach just two inches in height. This will allow room for the roots to spread and have sufficient space for the feathery leaves when they are mature.

The plant will also self-sow easily and abundantly if the ripe seeds are left to dry on the plant. They will fall to the ground in mid summer, germinate over the winter months, and begin new seedlings the next spring. These will need to be moved to your desired location, however, because the taproots will develop fairly quickly and penetrate deeply into the soil.

Transplanting one year old seedlings is another method of propagation. These seedlings might come from a friend, a nursery start, or some potted seeds you have encouraged over the winter months. These small plants can be transplanted because the taproot is not yet fully developed. Always plant into a partly shady location with good, moist garden soil. Seedlings should be placed at least eighteen inches apart. Propagating new plants from seedlings is an almost fail-safe way to increase your supply or start a friend on Sweet Cicely. My young friend, Briana Howatson, has started several seedlings of her favorite herb, Sweet Cicely, and she now has her own supply of licorice seeds.

Culinary Uses

As I noted earlier, all parts of the Sweet Cicely plant are edible — and delicious! Use fresh leaves as soon as they unfold in the spring and continue harvesting until late fall. The leaf is mild-flavored with a hint of aniseed. This marvelous plant is particularly good for diabetics or persons wanting to cut down on calories in their diet because it can replace one half or more of the sugar required in recipes. It additionally reduces the acidity and tartness in fruits. I recently used it to reduce the sugar by half in a blueberry pie for my computer friend, David Battey. He wondered what brought out the flavor of the usually bland blueberries, and I had to admit it was my favorite sugar-saver herb, Sweet Cicely. This herb can be used generously in this way. Try it on rhubarb, fruit salads, stewed prunes, currants and as a licorice-flavored liquid in fruit pies or compotes. Since I dehydrate many fruits from our garden, I use Sweet Cicely as a flavored water or syrup to rehydrate the fruit. It's also good in summer drinks in addition to the ice water I usually gulp.

I have given you a wonderful Apple and Sweet Cicely Tart recipe that I hope you will try. This was given to me by two friends from Lake Stevens, Washington. They tell the story of serving this scrumptious creation as a luncheon dessert to forty women. After the lunch, the only food the guests talked about was this very unusual 'pie.' One lady suggested the green flakes were likely parsley! Probably the only herb with which she was familiar. I'll bet all forty ladies are now advocates of Sweet Cicely.

The delicate sweet quality of this plant offsets nicely the taste of brussels sprouts, cabbage, parsnips, turnips, and potatoes. Try adding it to soups and stews, or chop the leaves finely for green salads. It will lend its own sweetness and clarity to the other greens and garnishes. This sweet-saver herb is equally good in salad dressings for fruit or green salads. I especially like it finely chopped over cooked carrots (sprinkled on just before serving) or in cream soups like potato, or beet soup. Sweet Cicely imparts an unusual flavor to beef or lamb stews and in omelettes.

Try pressing the young cicely leaves into a fresh fish steak, such as marlin, tuna, or sablefish and then grill. It can add a freshly sweet licorice flavor to fish or fish sauces. I have also used it on a variety of poultry dishes with very good results.

The leaves or seeds are an important ingredient in a *bouquet garni*. The green seeds are great in fruit or potato salads and in avocado dressings. The seeds are also used to make candy, syrups, liqueurs and cakes. An oil is extracted from the seeds to flavor the liqueurs or you can do this simply by steeping immature green seeds in vodka to make a licorice-flavored drink.

The root is edible as well and can be grated and added to quick breads and muffins much like shredded zucchini. Sweet Cicely seeds can be bruised and substituted for caraway seeds in baking breads and desserts. You might want to try boiling the root, slice it and serve cold with salad oil. It is also delicious as an ingredient in stir-fry dishes.

Sweet Cicely is a wonderful garnish on the plate whether with an entrée, a beverage or dessert. Try its many and varied uses, fresh, eight months of the year. That in itself, is quite extraordinary.

Medicinal Uses

With all of those culinary uses mentioned above, it's amazing that it has medicinal uses as well. Sweet Cicely does play a minor role as a medicinal herb as all parts of the plant have been used in helpful preparations, and it does have many uses in the home.

Historically, the roots were boiled until tender and given to the elderly to eat, believing it would strengthen their digestion as well as their bodies. It has also been used for many years as a tonic for young girls for an overall good feeling of youth and sometimes to increase the appetite.

A Sweet Cicely tea made from young fresh leaves is used for digestion and to relieve flatulence. Intestinal gas can sometimes be caused by eating too many root vegetables. If this is a problem for you or someone close to you, try eliminating those for awhile to see if it helps. Eating Sweet Cicely on a daily basis will help prevent indigestion and can increase appetite for those who need a stimulant. A wholesome tonic can be made by infusing the root in brandy for aiding digestion.

Chewing the immature green seeds is another way to achieve this digestive action. In addition to being a gentle stimulant for digestive upsets, it is equally effective for coughs. An infusion of bruised seeds as tea is a good expectorant.

The roots of the plant also carry antiseptic properties. A decoction made from these antiseptic roots was used externally for snake and dog bites and in ointment for wounds and ulcers.

Although its uses have not been scientifically tested, Sweet Cicely has been used in folk medicine for many years in parts of the world. Some old herbalists thought that Sweet Cicely was so harmless that you could not use it amiss. Because Sweet Cicely is harmless when used medicinally, it adds to its lack of reputation as a good medicinal herb.

? Other Uses

My favorite way of utilizing Sweet Cicely is in floral arrangements. When the lovely long fronds are cut and placed in a garden bouquet, they add a delicate shape and hold up better than any fern in my ample garden. I have had Sweet Cicely leaves last for several weeks by cutting an additional one quarter inch from the bottom every few days to allow the stems to continue to take up water. Remember the stems are hollow, unlike ferns, therefore they have a great capacity to hold water and freshness.

Dried flower heads with the seeds intact are also pretty in winter arrangements. Dried leaves and flowers can be used in *potpourri* and sachets. Because of the unusual texture and shape, the leaves are used in a dry form to decorate paper and candles, herb prints, and *decoupage*.

Commercially, the oil from the Sweet Cicely seeds is used to flavor *Chartreuse* and other liqueurs. And of course, the mature black seeds are used for furniture polish which gives a glossy finish and aromatic smell to all fine woods.

 # Recipes

Apple & Sweet Cicely Tart *(From The Magic Of Herbs)*

For the tart pastry, cut six ounces of **unsalted butter** into one and two thirds cup **flour** and three tablespoons of **superfine sugar**. (This sugar can be made by whirling the sugar for several seconds in a kitchen processor fitted with a metal blade .) Stir in one **egg yolk** and enough **cold water** to make a firm dough. Let this dough rest for thirty minutes. Cook one and one half pounds of **apples** (peeled, cored and sliced) in a saucepan with one quarter cup of **butter** and six tablespoons of **sugar** for about ten minutes, until tender. Remove from the heat, and add the grated **zest and juice of one lemon** and let cool. Roll out the pastry dough and line a ten-inch spring-form pan or other straight-sided pan. Leave enough extra dough to form lattice strips for the top of the tart. Bake the pastry in the oven at 400° F. for fifteen minutes and remove. Stir a handful of chopped **Sweet Cicely** into the cooled apple mixture and pour into the pastry crust. Make lattice strips from remaining dough and cut one half inch wide. Weave the strips over and under each other on top of the tart. Return to the oven and bake an additional fifteen minutes until the pastry is golden and the filling is bubbling. Sprinkle the surface with sifted **confectioner's sugar**.

Sweet Cicely Applesauce

Place one and one half pounds of cooking **apples**, cut into quarters, in a heavy pan with enough **water** to cover the bottom. Cook slowly with the lid on until tender and soft. Sieve the apple mixture through a food mill. While still warm, stir in one tablespoon of chopped fresh **Sweet Cicely** and a little **sugar** (depending on the sweetness of the apples). This can be served cold with **whipped cream** or frozen in containers for later use.

Fruit Salad with Sweet Cicely

Mix together small pieces of four or five of your **favorite fruits** in season. Choices might include strawberries, melons, grapes, pears, peaches, plums, oranges, kiwis, etc. For a quick dressing, blend **juices** from oranges, lemons and/or limes with two tablespoons of chopped fresh **cicely leaves** or immature seeds and one tablespoon of **sugar**. Serve cold.

Rhubarb-Strawberry Jam with Sweet Cicely

Wash and slice **rhubarb** thinly to make one pound. Cook with one quarter cup water a couple of minutes until tender. Add two and one half cups of crushed, washed and destemmed **strawberries** to rhubarb mixture. Add five cups **sugar** and one cup minced **Sweet Cicely** leaves and stir well. Place on high heat and, stirring constantly, bring to full boil. Boil hard one minute while continually stirring. Remove from heat and stir in one half bottle of **liquid pectin**. Skim the foam and fill half pint jars. Seal the jars and process in water bath for five minutes. Makes 7-8 1/2 pint jars.

Fruit & Melon Soup With Cicely

Remove flesh from one whole **watermelon**. Remove seeds and discard. Place chunked watermelon and juice of ten **oranges** in a pot and bring to a boil. Turn to simmer and add one **cinnamon stick** (broken into pieces), one quarter teaspoon **allspice** and one half teaspoon of **cardamon powder**. Continue heating liquid, covered, 45 minutes. Meanwhile, place one quarter cup of coarsely chopped **dried apricots** in saucepan with enough **water** to cover. Bring liquid to a boil, turn to simmer and cook until fruit is very soft (20-30 minutes). Cool slightly, turn contents into a blender and puree. Set aside. Add three quarter pound of mixed **fresh fruit** (apples, bananas, pears, pineapple), one-half cup **dark raisins** and one quarter cup **golden raisins** to simmering fruit juice during last fifteen minutes. In last five minutes add one half pound of **fresh berries** (strawberries, blueberries, raspberries) and one half cup of chopped fresh **Sweet Cicely** leaves. Remove cinnamon sticks and add one quarter cup each of **honey and lemon juice** and stir well. Garnish portions in individual bowls with **yogurt** and **Sweet Cicely sprigs** or flowers.

Vegetable Medley with Sweet Cicely

Dice two cups each of fresh, peeled **carrots, rutabaga or turnips** and steam until tender. Serve with melted butter and one half cup of raw, unripe **Sweet Cicely seeds**, slightly bruised.

Sweet Cicely and Rose Geranium Sorbet

(Ron Zimmerman of The Herbfarm)

Combine three and one half cups **water** with one and one quarter cup **sugar** in a saucepan and bring to a boil. Boil five minutes and cool to room temperature. Place 24 leaves each of **Rose Geranium** and six-inch sprigs of **Sweet Cicely** with another three-eighths cup of **sugar** in a food processor fitted with a steel blade. Process three to four minutes. Combine the herbal puree with the cooled syrup, stir, and let stand one hour. Strain out the herb leaves by putting the sorbet mixture through a fine sieve or several layers of cheesecloth. Add one half cup **lemon juice.** Freeze in an ice cream freezer, or pour the mixture in a metal bowl and place it in the freezer. Scrape down the side every hour or so until the sorbet is fully frozen, 3-4 hours.

Stewed Fruit with Cicely

When stewing fresh or dried fruits (**plums, pears, apples, apricots**), use this liquid blend instead of water. Add one tablespoon of chopped fresh **cicely leaves** and one teaspoon **sugar** to one cup of **water** and boil. Remove the herb, add the fruit and simmer until fruit is soft. Try a blend of **mint and/or Lemon Balm with Sweet Cicely** for herb poaching or simmering.

Cookies — sprinkle crushed, dried **Sweet Cicely seeds** on cookies before baking for a licorice flavor.

Sweet Cicely Furniture Polish

Pound fresh, green **Sweet Cicely seeds** in a mortar with a pestle. Place a handful of these bruised seeds in a soft cloth and rub on wood as a polish. Or try grinding ripe seeds into a powder and polish wooden floors or furniture.

Other Notes

I grow this unique herb mostly for its beautiful ornamental form and shape, as well as for its great licorice seeds. It is stunning in the garden with its feathery leaves and white clusters of flowers. The neighborhood children know when those seeds are ready for eating because they flock to the bush as bees to the hive. That's all right with me, because I probably wouldn't have time to cut them all off before they reseeded! This is definitely the favorite herb of the children in my neighborhood.

If you are a composter of your garden wastes, you might like to try planting Sweet Cicely plants around your compost pile. It not only hides the pile but appears as a lovely ring of green and white — a delight to the eyes as well as the nose!

Sweet Cicely is usually only available from your own garden or a friend's. Most nurseries do not sell this herb fresh or in a preserved form. I hope you will get one today and start your own licorice, sugar-saver plant.

Notes:

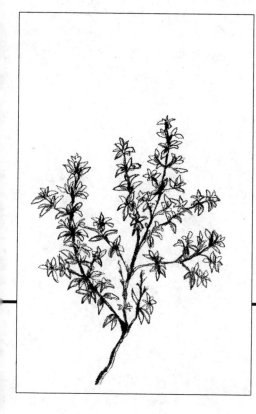

Thyme

*The Perfect
Culinary Herb*

Thyme

T hyme (pronounced time) is the favorite herb of many cooks. It is supposed to dispel melancholy, which is probably the reason that French cooks are so pleasant. There are more than one hundred species and four hundred named cultivars of this revered plant. _Thymus_ is the Greek word for courage; throughout history, thyme has been associated with strength, bravery, energy and happiness.

The generic name may also be from the Greek, _thymon_, 'to fumigate' as it was used as a sweet-smelling incense. The common spelling of thyme is Greek and means to burn a sacrifice.

Thyme is quite modest in appearance as it grows hugging the ground but it pungently perfumes the air overhead. The plant is symmetrical, plump and creeping and has many uses and functions. In the garden, thyme is used as a ground cover, between stepping stones, to fill cracks in a rockery, as a front border, or simply as a fragrant garden for relaxing. Uses in the home include thyme as a culinary flavoring, ornamentally for sachets, _potpourri_ and wreaths, and medicinally in teas for indigestion. This endearing little herb scents everything around it — whether in the garden, the kitchen or a decorative bouquet. Thyme is considered by many to be the perfect plant because of its myriad varieties, colors, uses, and aromas.

Botanical Name

This large genus has more than 100 species and over 400 named cultivars. All garden varieties of *Thymus vulgaris* are culinary. These varieties include Common Thyme and Garden Thyme. Common Thyme has the strongest scent and flavor. Three principal varieties of common thyme are: English or variegated leaf thyme; German or broad-leaf thyme; and French summer or narrow leaf thyme, sometimes called 'Provencal', with tiny gray pointed leaves. Each is distinguished by the shape of its leaves and the plants grow from one to twelve inches in height.

Thyme plants can generally be sorted into categories by size and growing habits; bush, semi-bush, creeping, and semi-creeping. The more prostrate and creeping varieties are used in landscaping and decorative purposes, whereas the more bushy and upright are used in cooking and medicinal uses.

Bush

Garden or Common Thyme — *Thymus vulgaris* — grows wild in dry, gravelly soil and on rocky ground. These aromatic plants with strong roots and woody, branched stems, have pale mauve flowers.

Silver Thyme — *T. x citriodorus* 'Silver Queen' — has a mild flavor and aroma that is superb for cooking. This 12 inch tall plant is eye-catching and makes a grand edging or border.

Silver Edged Thyme — *T. x citriodorus* 'Variegatus' — has pink flowers and silver variegated leaves. It is a particularly attractive plant for a silver garden when mixed with lavender, santolina and artemisia.

Silver Lemon Thyme — *T. x citriodorus* 'Argenteus' — is a shrublike thyme similar to Golden Lemon Thyme having bright green leaves that are highly lemon-scented and edged with a silver margin. Its flowers are pale lilac.

Golden Lemon Thyme — *T. x citriodorus* 'Aureas' — is a bushy lemon-scented plant with a pink cast of flowers and golden foliage. This is a charming, low-growing shrub about 12 inches tall with pretty little branches of green and brilliant yellow, glossy, rounded leaves with an intense bouquet of citrus and spice. The variegation is less pronounced during hot, sunny weather. This variety is less hardy than Garden Thyme and struggles in wet winters.

Semi-Bush

Mother-of-Thyme — *T.praecox spp. arcticus* — is considered by some as the best small thyme to grow between bricks or stone, near walkways, in a rock garden or on terraces because of its tough, creeping nature. This species has a carpet-like growth, but grows a little taller than the creeping varieties. This Wild Thyme is thought to be one of the oldest varieties. Colors include red, white or pink flowered forms.

Creeping

Wild Thyme — *T. serpyllum* — has numerous varieties that differ in flower color from white to lavender, and crimson to pink. It is a shrubby perennial with a woody fibrous root and long creeping stems; mostly grown as an ornamental. It's a tough species with stems only one to three inches tall. Varieties include *T. serpyllum* 'Snowdrift' (a creeper with white flowers and faintly scented leaves); *T. serpyllum* 'Lemon Curd' (a creeper with pink flowers, long branches and lemon-scented green leaves); *T. serpyllum albus* (with white flowers and bright green leaves); *T. serpyllum aureas* (a creeping thyme with mauve flowers and mildly scented leaves); *T.serpyllum* 'Minor' (a dwarf creeper with pink flowers and tiny green leaves that is very slow-growing); and *T. serpyllum* 'Pink Chintz' (a creeper with pink flowers and large strongly lemon-scented green leaves).

Doone Valley Thyme — *T.* 'Doone Valley' — is a creeper with pale purple flowers and lemon-scented, dark green leaves with gold splashes.

Green Lemon Thyme — *T. x citriodorus* — has deep green leaves and is a rapid grower that will root where the stems lay on the ground. This 12 inch tall plant forms a lovely mound with a lemon aroma that is especially good in chicken and fish dishes or salads. It is winter hardy and can be used in *potpourri* as well.

Golden Thyme — *T. x citriodorus* 'Archers Gold' — is a dwarf creeping shrub intensely gold most of the year.

Golden Lemon Thyme — *T. x citriodorus* 'Bertram Anderson' — has small mounds of golden green leaves and a pink cast. Lightly shearing Lemon Thyme in the spring will cause it to grow 12-15 inches tall. This variety makes a good herbal butter.

White Creeping Thyme — *T. praecox. spp. arcticus* 'Albus' — has white flowers and tiny, bright green leaves. This cultivar is a good variety for a moss-covered hanging basket or a ground cover — especially as a lush carpet for the bees.

Crimson Thyme — *T. praecox* 'Coccineus' — is a creeper with vivid magenta flowers. This variety looks especially good with silver-foliaged plants in the foreground of a bed. It can be used to flavor soups and stews but more generally is used as an essential oil.

Red Thyme — *T. praecox* 'Splendens' — has reddish winter foliage and grows to four inches. This variety makes a good ground cover.

Woolly Thyme — *T. pseudolanuginosus* — has a sea of tiny, rose pink flowers and silver gray-green, hairy leaves. This two inch tall variety is very drought resistant, and is generally used in rock gardens or among paving stones and along walkways. This hardy silvery-gray plant spreads readily and is not a culinary variety.

Golden Creeping Thyme — *T. praecox spp. arcticus* 'Aureas' — is a low, bushy thyme with little aroma. The colorful pink flowers appear on the mature plants. Growing just four to six inches tall, it creeps across the ground and roots where the stems touch the soil. As a ground cover it should be used in a sunny or partly sunny area. It also does well in hanging baskets.

Semi-Creeping

Caraway Thyme — *T. herba-barona* — has pink flowers and is caraway-scented with tiny, tasty leaves. This reliable creeper is durable and fragrant and can be used as a lawn herb. See the Other Notes section for more information.

Camphor Thyme — *T. camphoratus* — is a six to twelve inch tall compact plant having dark green leaves, a camphor scent, and requiring a dry climate. It is a tender perennial that can be used in *potpourri* and dried wreaths, but is not generally used for culinary dishes.

Thyme is a member of the *Labiatae family* and is a relative of basil, marjoram, oregano and mint.

History

It was the best of thymes, it was the worst of thymes...As early as 5,000 years ago, thyme was mentioned for medicinal uses in the Sumerian culture. Native to Southern Europe and the western Mediterranean region, thyme is now widely cultivated.

Many cultures throughout history have used this impressive and worthwhile herb. Romans used thyme medicinally as a cough remedy, digestive aid and treatment for intestinal worms. The Roman soldiers bathed in thyme water to give themselves vigor. Charlemagne ordered thyme grown in all the imperial gardens for its culinary and medicinal values. Medieval German herbalist, Hildegard of Bingen, considered it the herb of choice for skin problems because of its antiseptic properties. From the 15-17th centuries thyme was used to combat the European plagues. During the Middle Ages, when thyme became linked to courage, noblewomen embroidered sprigs of thyme on scarves and gave them to their favorite knights leaving for the Crusades.

The English during the Renaissance loved thyme in a social context as it was a compliment to be told that you were, 'as sweet as thyme.' The Spanish, Italian and French used thyme fields for grazing their sheep and goats because of the wonderful flavor it gave to the meat. Caraway Thyme was imported from Corsica and Sicily for use in beef dishes in Europe before it was ever grown there.

Thyme has been cultivated since the days of ancient Greece for its strongly aromatic, slightly pungent foliage. It grows wild on

188 Herbs You Can Master
188 Herbs You Can Master

Mount Hymettus in Greece, and the Greeks embrace this little herb wholeheartedly. In Columbus' day, long before mariners of Genoa could see their land from the sea, their noses smelled the thyme that blanketed the native Ligurian hills. They knew land was near when the thyme and rosemary growing on the headlands of the Mediterranean helped them "smell" their way home. Scottish highlanders drank tea of Wild Thyme to give themselves strength and courage and to prevent nightmares. The Egyptians used thyme for embalming, and it has been used to sprinkle on sacrificial animals to make them more acceptable to the gods. It was also burned to chase stinging insects from the house and used in a sleep pillow because it was thought to relieve both epilepsy and melancholy, as well as preventing the aforementioned nightmares.

In World War I, thyme's essential oil, thymol, was used on the battlefield as an antiseptic. There was a major thymol crisis during this time because most of the world's supply was distilled in Germany. When the British and French declared war on Germany, they had to scramble to overcome a terrible shortage of the suddenly vital antiseptic.

Thyme will tell...In folklore, thyme is said to be the nest or home to fairies, and patches of thyme were set aside for this purpose. (I have not yet seen any fairies in my thyme patches although I have looked for them several times. I do find many bees, however.) If you drank a beer with thyme it was said to cure shyness. Or you could sip a cup of soup made of beer and thyme for the same malady. I suspect the beer, not the thyme, however, had more to do with getting rid of shyness.

Thyme was brought to the New World by the earliest European settlers and it now grows wild in some areas. In New York it was imported through seeds which adhered to the fleece of sheep from Greece, and Western Massachusetts also has naturalized patches. Thyme honey continues to be a favorite in these areas as well as in my corner of the world. I made a batch of thyme honey recently and it tasted so delicious that I have given you the recipe in the Recipe section.

Today many Americans might be surprised to find commercial products in their own medicine chests made with thyme oils...Listerine, Vicks VapoRub, etc. Even though the plant has been replaced by more potent germ fighters, its volatile oil is still used in antiseptics, mouthwashes, cough remedies, and digestive aids.

 TYPE: Perennial *(semi-hardy)*

Although this plant is certainly considered a perennial, some varieties need winter protection in colder climates. Lemon Thyme rarely survives a winter, however, as it is quite tender and does not like a wet climate. Thyme grows well throughout the United States with the exception of the humid Gulf states.

Description

Common Thyme, <u>*Thymus vulgaris,*</u> and all of its species and varieties need full sun, and coarse, well-drained, rocky soil.

All thymes have thin, woody, twig-like stems with tiny, oval, aromatic leaves that are slightly hairy underneath. This bushy, prostrate, evergreen shrub's root structure is made up of fine grayish-brown roots that form a dense mat.

This dainty little plant grows compactly from one to twelve inches in height depending on the variety. The more upright, bushy varieties grow from eight to twelve inches tall, and the creeping or low-growing varieties from one to ten inches tall. Their squarish stems usually become woody in the second season. Varieties can be differentiated by the size and intensity of their scented leaves, their upright or prostrate growing habit, and of course the flowers.

The tiny flowers of the thyme plants may be white, pale pink, or purple, depending on the variety. Clusters of these flowers usually bloom in June and July. Because the bees particularly love this herb when in bloom, honey made from it is especially appetizing. Many herb gardeners become beekeepers, as well, so they may enjoy this particular variety of pure, sweet honey.

The upright, bushy thymes are the best for culinary purposes. Some thymes taste and smell like lemon, mint, pine, balsam, licorice, caraway, or nutmeg. Their flavor is generally used sparingly in dishes as a background seasoning or accompaniment with other herbs. My personal favorites for flavor are Orange Balsam, Silver Thyme, Lemon Thyme, Caraway, and Oregano Thyme, with the latter two having the most unique flavors. Orange Balsam Thyme has a distinct citrus, pine scent and taste, with narrow, sparse leaves on a small upright plant. The small, tight, ground-hugging Caraway Thyme forms a mat about six inches wide, with very small, shiny, narrow-pointed leaves. With its pink flowers and caraway flavor, it is a delightful little plant whether used ornamentally or in cooking. Oregano Thyme forms an eight-inch wide mat, with rounded green leaves shaded with mahogany overtones. The flavor is an aromatic cross between oregano and thyme and is a semi-creeping variety. Each of these is special and well worth growing in your garden.

Creeping Thymes in dozens of varieties are small ground cover plants, and usually grown as ornamentals in banks and rock gardens or between flagstones. The flower colors range from purple through red, lavender, pink, and white. Varieties include woolly, yellow-edged leaves, silver-edged leaves, caraway, nutmeg, Doone Valley, and many others.

 ## Planting & Care Requirements

Thyme waits for no man — or woman for that matter. Plant one or more now for a heavenly-scented garden. These plants are truly great in a fragrance garden as a low border.

Thyme should be planted 12-18 inches apart in full sun. It will tolerate some partial shade, however, once the plant is established. It requires good air circulation, and good drainage. Light, dryish (somewhat poor or sandy) well-drained, alkaline soil with a ph of 5.5 to 7.0 is ideal. A tablespoon of cottonseed or bone meal around the base of each plant gives it nutritious encouragement for growth. Do not feed again until the following spring, however, because too rapid of growth sets the plant up for winterkill. Although some people think that herbs, especially thyme, thrive in poor soils, they really do need nutrients with moderate amounts of organic matter or fertilizer to supply these nutrients. Even though thyme grows in rocky crevices, a lack of nutrients will produce only a few spindly stems rather than a healthy bushy plant. The tiny roots of this herb are subject to root rot or fungal disease if the soil is too soggy in winter. Thyme likes a dry environment and is considered one of the drought tolerant herbs.

During the colder winter months in our area, it is usually necessary to cover plants with a layer of mulch of pine needles or criss-crossed tree branches from a Christmas tree. The plants need to be kept cold in the winter to prevent repeated freezing and thawing which can cause the plants to push up out of the earth and precipitate root damage. You should not use a mulch such as leaves or grass clippings that will hold water or mat down. Remove the mulch branches when the first new sprouts appear in the spring. If temperatures drop below 10 F. you may lose the thyme anyway. Creeping thymes can withstand winter temperatures much better than the bush varieties.

When uncovering the mulched plants in the spring, trim the stems back to half of the previous year's growth to encourage a denser growth habit, but not below the leaves unless there is new growth showing. Thyme becomes woody and less fragrant after several years unless young growth is encouraged by spring pruning. Replace the plants every 2-3 years if they get very woody or when the center dies.

These plants also do very well indoors. To bring thyme plants indoors for the winter, dig up the plants at least one month before the first expected frost. Set them in pots one inch larger than the ball of soil around the roots (usually a 6" pot is ideal). Use a potting soil that is coarse with some lime chips. Cut back one third to one half of the top growth to compensate for roots damaged in digging and transplanting. Keep these plants in the shade for 7-10 days to give them a chance to recover, and then gradually move them indoors. Grown indoors, thyme needs five hours of strong, direct sunlight a day. Water the plants until moist but not soggy and allow them to dry between watering.

Wild Thyme can be planted between rocks or as a ground cover spacing plants ten inches apart. These low, bushy plants have lovely blooms that are attractive in a foreground. Creeping Thymes can be successfully planted in cinder blocks with the different varieties planted in individual holes. They will flow over the sides in a variety of textures and colors. Creeping Thymes are also excellent for hanging indoor planters, and the trailing varieties are wonderful in strawberry jar gardens for porches or balconies. Bushy thymes do well in indoor planters but try to approximate their native soil by supplementing commercial potting soil with lime chips or coarse sand. Keep them snipped for culinary uses and to preserve their shape and continual growing.

Common Thyme is more successful for beginners to grow than some other finicky species, such as Lemon or Caraway Thymes.

Spider mites sometimes are a nuisance to thyme plants. Spray with insecticidal soap for these nuisance critters. To prevent or lessen the problem of fungal disease, place plants several inches apart. Good air circulation and drainage are the best prevention.

Harvesting

Our thyme clocks tell us when it's thyme to harvest. One full cutting can be made for preserving when the flowers just begin to open. The leaves are the most aromatic and sweet at this time. The bushy thymes can also be harvested when they are in full flower. This keeps them short and dense with a good flush of growth in summer. This growth can be left to help the plant survive the winter.

Some people like to take a complete second cutting to within a few inches of the ground during late fall but this will make your thyme plants *much* less winter hardy. When harvesting thyme in late summer, I remove no more than a third of the stem, so the plant will not be encouraged to make tender growth that may not survive the winter.

For three harvests during a season, cut one third of the plant in early spring, cut again when buds form *or* at flowering time and take a final harvest about 45 days before the first frost. You can harvest the first year about six weeks after transplanting leaving the stems about two inches long.

For an ongoing supply of fresh thyme during the growing season, keep the stem tips well pruned by removing one half of the current season growth. This will encourage a bushy, healthy plant. You may cut whole stems when needed for recipes. In early spring, trim the stems of Lemon and Common Thyme back to half of the previous year's growth to encourage a more dense plant. The flowers can also be harvested and dried for sachets and *potpourri*. During a hot humid summer, thyme can be cut heavily.

When harvesting the leaves for cooking, trim the stems and wash the leaves if necessary.

One mature thyme plant will usually produce about one half cup of fresh leaves at each of two or three harvests in a season.

 ## Preservation

Thyme is of the essence, and its essence can certainly be preserved. After harvesting, thyme may be preserved by drying, freezing, or placing in vinegar, butter, oil or honey. All are excellent ways to enjoy the thyme flavor throughout the winter months.

To dry thyme, you may either place on paper towels in a warm room, use a dehydrator, or hang upside down in bunches. I prefer to use a dehydrator for thyme like other short-stemmed, wiry herbs because I find them difficult to tie into bundles for hanging. Dry the leaves while they are still on the stems. After drying, the leaves can be removed easily by running your thumb and forefinger from top to bottom of the stem. Discard the stems as they have no flavor on their own. Dry the leaves until crisp but not crumbly. Don't crush the dried leaves. Store them whole in a jar and crush them just before using them to release the potent flavor. Thyme leaves hold their flavor better than most herbs when dried. The dried leaves have a stronger flavor than the fresh ones.

Thyme can be preserved in vinegar, butter, honey or oil as well. For butter, oil, or vinegar, use the same process as described in earlier chapters. For thyme honey, see the Recipe section in this chapter.

Thyme leaves freeze well also. It is best to remove the clean leaves from the stems before freezing. To do this when the leaves are fresh, it is necessary to hold the tender tops of each stem and run your thumb and forefinger down the stems. Although the tips break easily and this process is thyme-consuming, it is well worth the effort to have a year around supply of this wonderfully tangy herb.

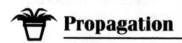 **Propagation**

It's only a matter of thyme — and practice — before you learn to create more plants. Cuttings or layering are the favored methods for multiplying these plants. Propagating by seed is the least dependable choice as many thymes are 'sports' and will not come true from seed.

Cuttings are best taken in spring but can be done a little later in the season as well. Snip a three to four inch stem of new growth from a healthy branch and include a piece of 'heel' of the woody stem. Strip the leaves from the bottom of the stem, dip in a rooting hormone if you wish, and place in wet sand. Roots should appear in about two weeks. To test for root development, watch for new top growth to appear. Give the plant a little tug. If it is fairly firm, new roots have developed and its time (thyme) to plant in small pots with a good potting soil or directly into the garden.

Layering is the best method of propagation only for Wild Thyme. For soil layering, bury a woody stem and cut it off after it has rooted. For simple layering, make an incision just below a node on the stem, cutting at a slant halfway through the branch. An alternative method is to scrape away the outer layer of bark instead of making an incision. Pin the branch down with a length of wire. In six to eight weeks, check for root growth by moving soil away from the wound.

Stool or mound layering can also be done by placing soil up to the lowest leaves on the stems. After several months, new roots may grow just below the surface. This plant can be trimmed below the new root level and transplanted and the lower roots will develop an additional plant. This type of propagation can be problematical, however, and should be attempted only if you have lots of patience and don't mind losing a few plants along the way.

Thyme can be started from seed, but these can be unpredictable in variety and usually include a mixture of species. It is common to have seed packets produce many inferior hybrids.

If choosing to propagate by seed, thyme is best started indoors about eight weeks before the last expected frost. You may, however, start them outdoors in the spring where the soil drains well and a somewhat steady soil temperature can be maintained. Germination can be slow outdoors. The tiny, round seeds keep their germinating power for up to three years. If started in a pot indoors, plant one quarter inch deep. Use a mixture of perlite, sand, peat moss and loam as a potting mix, and cover the seeds with fine sand. They may germinate within seven days if kept misted and at a fairly steady 70° F. Once these 'starts' are four inches high, place them outdoors in a sheltered but sunny location. Move them into the permanent garden a week or two later. Thyme takes about two years to reach a really usable size. This is the reason it is usually propagated by stem cuttings.

If you bring a thyme plant indoors for the winter months, dig up an entire plant one month before the first frost. If the plant is large this is a good time to create additional plants by division. Put the plant in a pot about one inch larger than the ball of soil around the roots. Cut back one third to one half of the top growth to compensate for roots damaged in digging. Keep the plants in the shade for a week to 10 days to give them a chance to recover, then gradually move them into full sun until time to take them indoors. Cut off worn out foliage at the soil level to encourage vigorous new growth.

⊎🍴 Culinary Uses

When in doubt, use thyme. It is compatible with many types of food. Although thyme has been better known and more used as a medicinal and decorative herb, it is fast becoming a favorite culinary herb as well. Thyme is a principal ingredient in French, Creole and Cajun cuisines and an essential ingredient of the classic seasoning *bouquet garni*, along with parsley and bay leaf. A basic thyme *bouquet garni* can be found in the Recipe section of this chapter.

Thyme and bay leaf go together like Abbott and Costello (each unique, but together even better.) Parsley and thyme together is a great taste treat of two well-matched herbs whether used in stuffing, in water to boil chicken, in fruit salad, jellies, custard, flavored honey or butters. Used in *fines herbes* of French cuisine, the sprigs of thyme are used in salads, clam chowder, and seafood gumbos.

Thyme has a reasonably strong flavor and should be used judiciously. It is best not to use thyme in combinations with rosemary and sage as each of these three have pungent and distinctive flavors. These competing flavors will clash in your foods. Thyme does, however, blend very nicely with chives, chervil, parsley, basil, marjoram, lemon, garlic or savory.

Thyme has a faint clove aftertaste and one fresh sprig is equal to one half teaspoon of ground dried thyme. Many chefs believe that French, English, and Greek thyme have the best flavor for culinary dishes.

As a meat preservative in ancient times, thyme was sprinkled on sacrificial animals to make them more acceptable to the gods.

This herb was introduced into cooking originally because of its meat-preserving action.

Use many thyme varieties to flavor any meat — beef, veal, lamb, poultry and rabbit, fish, sausages and *patés*. This dainty, fragrant herb is also outstanding in poultry stuffing, soups, casseroles, stews, breads, herb butters and mayonnaise. It is used with many vegetables, including cucumbers, tomatoes, onions, carrots, parsnips, leeks, mushrooms, asparagus, green beans, lentils, broccoli, potatoes, corn, and peas. Nutritious éntrees of grain and rice, pasta and dry beans go very well with the distinctive flavor of thyme.

When using fresh thyme, cut sprigs and keep the stems in water until ready to use. Strip the leaves from the stem by holding it upright by its fragile tip and run the thumb and forefinger of the opposite hand down, stripping off the leaves and any florets that might be attached. These leaves may be used whole or minced into smaller pieces. When using thyme is soups, stews, gumbos, etc. I usually place the whole stem in the pot. The leaves will come off during the cooking and the stems can be easily removed by hand.

The flowers of thyme, like the leaves, are sweet and savory with an earthy aroma, though the flowers tend to be a bit milder with more of a floral scent. The tiny blossoms are a tasty and attractive garnish to salads, vegetables, and soups, and give a nice accent to desserts, like fruit compotes. I also use them in butters and sauces.

Lemon and Caraway Thyme are handsome plants and taste like lemon and caraway, respectively, when used fresh. These flavor characteristics nearly disappear in cooking, however. Lemon Thyme is a natural paired with any chicken dish you can think of, a perfect herb for seasoning fish, and adds a lemony lift to all vegetables, especially green beans and zucchini. Since the taste partly dissipates when over-heated, I add the herb at the last moment of cooking time. Lemon Thyme also makes a delicious herb butter and is a pleasing surprise in sugar cookies and tea cakes.

Caraway Thyme is another favorite but should be minced and sprinkled on when serving as it, too, loses much of its flavor when cooked. Try it raw on many vegetables such as cucumbers, tomatoes, onions, carrots, parsnips, leeks, mushrooms, asparagus, green beans, broccoli, potatoes, corn, or peas. Caraway and Oregano Thyme are particularly tasty in *pesto* when combined with parsley, sage or marjoram.

Creeping thymes have very little flavor and are not generally used in cooking or flavoring raw dishes.

Sprigs of thyme placed under *hors d'eouvers* on a tray give a delightful fragrance and taste to vegetables and cheeses. This herb continues to be popular in flavoring liqueurs and cheeses. Try sprigs in olive oil and artichoke brine. Strips of roasted bell pepper marinated in olive oil with minced garlic and thyme is really outstanding served over pasta or rice.

Thyme makes a stimulating tea as well. Try an equal amount of dried mint, rosemary, sage, thyme, marjoram, calendula flowers, and chamomile for a wonderful tea that is tasty, relaxing, and a real winter treat. Greek Thyme honey is famous and can be found in some organic food stores. See the Recipe section for a delicious thyme honey that I make each fall for winter pancakes and peanut butter sandwiches. Thyme syrup can be made by mixing our native honey with a strong thyme tea.

Medicinal Uses

Thyme heals all wounds...and this medicinal herb surely is a favorite for many healing uses.

The aromatic oil of thyme contains two chemicals — thymol and carvacrol — that account for its medicinal value. Both chemicals have preservative, antibacterial, and antifungal properties, as well as expectorant properties and may be useful as digestive aids.

Herbal medicine in Germany today uses thyme to relax the respiratory tract and treat coughs, even emphysema and whooping cough. Some feel that thyme is as effective for the respiratory system as Peppermint is to the digestive system. Test tube experiments support this traditional use of thyme as its expectorant properties are used as a carminative. It is used in cough syrups because it causes the membrane lining the respiratory tract to weep a watery secretion making it easier to cough up mucous. As a strengthener of the lungs, it helps with shortness of breath and congestion. Because of its decongesting qualities, it purges the body of phlegm and aids an assortment of bronchial problems and asthma.

Oil of thyme, or *thymol*, is a colorless to reddish brown liquid, having a sharp taste and peppery scent. This oil can be quite toxic if taken in a pure form. The oil of thyme is much more powerful as an antiseptic than a simple infusion of the leaves would be.

Thymol and carvacrol relax the smooth muscle tissue of the gastrointestinal tract, making this herb an antispasmodic. This antispasmodic action is also beneficial to relieve menstrual cramps by soothing the uterine muscles. If large amounts of the oil are used, however, it could be a uterine stimulant. *Because of this possibility, pregnant women should not use it in large amounts nor should children under two years of age.* Older children and people over 65 years of age should start with a low-strength preparation.

Use the thyme herb rather than its oil. Even a few teaspoons of thyme oil can be toxic, causing symptoms of headache, nausea, vomiting, muscular weakness, dizziness, thyroid impairment, and heart and respiratory depression. It can also have a depressing effect on body temperature. Persons with thyroid conditions should consult their physician before using thyme.

As a stimulant, thymol makes a good rubdown liniment because it causes a heating/soothing action. It can also, however, cause a rash on sensitive skin.

Thyme has a broad range of applications in the medicine chest by aiding digestion and intestinal pain from flatulence, easing stomach and menstrual cramps, soothing migraines, depression and nervousness, and acting as a stimulant for appetite.

Because of its antibacterial properties, thymus species oil is effective against salmonella, staph, streptococcus, and other germs.

Modern research has shown that thyme essence is so strong it can kill bacilli in forty seconds. As a tincture, you may safely take from one half to one teaspoon up to three times a day. After cleaning a wound, a tincture of a few drops of thyme can be used under the bandage as an antiseptic. Thyme may be made into a compress to soothe cuts, sores and wounds or the fresh leaves can be crushed and used on small cuts and scrapes.

Contemporary herbalists recommend a thymol infusion for sore throat, laryngitis, cough, whooping cough, and nervousness. As a mouthwash, thyme infusion tends to cure halitosis because it deodorizes. Headaches and nightmares can be decreased as well by a thyme infusion. Use thyme leaves before they flower for the best strength. Both leaves and flower tops can be used, however. An infusion can be made by using two tablespoons of fresh (or two teaspoons of dried) herb per cup of boiling water. Steep 10 minutes. This medicinal infusion can be consumed three times a day and has a pleasant aroma and faint clove-like aftertaste.

Using thyme tea or an infusion for indigestion is also very helpful and especially good with fatty foods that cause stomach distress. You may want to try boiling thyme leaves in wine to make a digestive tea for gastrointestinal flatulence complaints. This really does relax and comfort the stomach.

⟨?⟩ Other Uses

Thyme is on our side...because of its many uses in addition to culinary and medicinal. Used in cosmetics, thyme has several applications. However, thymol, the oil in thyme, can cause contact dermatitis, and therefore, should be tested before using in cosmetics or bath soaps. The sweet scent of thyme leaves makes an ideal base for fragrant herb cushions, *potpourri*, sleep pillows and sachets. For a fragrant and invigorating bath, place a small handful of thyme stems in cheesecloth and place under the spout so your bath water can pour directly over it. This bath is both stimulating and a gentle antiseptic cleanser.

Dried leaves and flower blossoms can be used for stuffing small pillows to help a mild depression or melancholy mood. Use thyme in sachets to preserve linens from insects.

The dried flowers used in wreaths serve as a good insect repellent and thyme even protects paper from mold. Bunches of dried thyme and flowers are wonderful as background on herbal wreaths. These can be used on straw or moss/wire wreaths. Thyme is also a favorite used in tussie-mussies, which are little floral bouquets.

Thyme plants really attract the bees with their beautiful flower displays and fragrance perfuming the air.

Oil of thyme is used in aromatherapy and in a comforting rub for rheumatism, sciatica and similar aches and pains because of thymol's heating action.

Boil thyme for ten minutes in water and use as a facial steam, hair rinse or gargle. Along with lavender and rosemary, thyme is one of the major strewing herbs.

In addition to being used in toothpaste, mouthwashes and as gargles, thyme is used in bath powders, scented soaps and *pot-pourri*. Thyme imparts a refreshing scent and color to herbal soap. See the Recipe section for a suggestion.

Thyme is a fumigant as well. Dried thyme leaves help preserve linens from insects. And as an antiseptic it kills mildew and mold.

 **Recipes**

Thyme Jelly

Place two cups of **thyme infusion** (see below), one quarter cup **vinegar or apple cider** and four and one half cups of **sugar** in a sauce pan and place over high heat until sugar is dissolved. After bringing to a boil, add one-half bottle **liquid pectin** and boil for one and one half minutes. Take off the heat. Add one or two drops of food coloring if desired. Fill sterilized jelly glasses with hot jelly and attach sealing lids. Place in hot water bath for five minutes. You may add a sprig of **thyme** to the top of each jar before sealing if you wish.

For infusion: add one cup of **fresh herbs** to two and one half cups boiling **water**. Let cool and strain the leaves from the liquid before using.

Thyme Honey

Layer three to five tablespoons of bruised **thyme** branches and leaves in the bottom of a saucepan. Cover with one and one-half cups of pure **honey** (unflavored). Heat over medium for three to four minutes or until honey is very fluid. Pour mixture into a glass jar and cover tightly with a lid. Turn upside down when mixture has cooled and every couple of days to continuing mixing the flavors. After seven to ten days, reheat the honey, remove the sprigs (leave a few leaves in) and place in jars and seal. (The honey can be reheated in the microwave with lid removed if you watch it carefully). This makes a wonderful gift.

Bouquet Garni *(For Soups & Stocks)*

Combine one-half cup of dried **parsley or chervil**, one **bay leaf** and one-quarter cup of dried **thyme**. For this dried *garni*, stitch the herbs in a cheesecloth bag or use a pull string top. For a *bouquet garni* with fresh herbs, simply tie a string around the stems of the herbs and place in cooking pot. Remove when the dish is completed. When using bay leaves, always remove them before serving the dish as hard bits of the leaf can cause damage to the esophagus or stomach lining. You might also want to try using chervil, tarragon, rosemary, basil or savory in these bags. Use sparingly in soups, stuffing, vegetables, jellies and fish.

Corn Sauté

Sauté three cups of fresh **corn kernels** and four sliced **green onions** in two tablespoons of **butter** until tender. Stir in one-half cup of **milk,** one teaspoon of **sugar,** a pinch of **salt and pepper** (optional) and cook over medium heat until sauce thickens. Add one tablespoon of fresh basil and one teaspoon of **fresh minced thyme.** Yields 6 servings.

Split Pea Soup with Thyme

Place two cups of quality **split peas** (green or yellow) and two quarts of **water** in a saucepan. Add one stalk of **celery** with top, chopped, one large **carrot,** washed and chopped, one medium **onion**, peeled and chopped, and several sprigs of fresh **thyme.** (Caraway, Orange Balsam, Silver or English are all very good). Add one **bay leaf,** whole (remember I said bay leaf and thyme go together like Abbot and Costello!), and a pinch of **cayenne or cajun spice.** Boil this mixture about twenty minutes and then simmer until peas are tender. When cool enough to handle remove the thyme stems and bay leaf and place remainder of soup in a blender and blend until smooth. This might take two or three batches to complete. Add salt and pepper if you wish, reheat and serve hot. This really is quite easy and the blending of ingredients at the end makes a wonderfully smooth soup. Makes about 8 servings

Clam Chowder with Thyme

I know everyone makes "the best" clam chowder, but this one really is and we have lots of good clam chowder restaurants in the Seattle area! The basic recipe for this was found in one of Jeff Smith's (The Frugal Gourmet) cookbooks.

Sauté two stalks of **celery** (with tops) chopped and one large **onion,** chopped, in two tablespoons of good **olive oil.** When wilted, but not browned, add six cups of homemade **chicken stock** (unsalted). While bringing stock to a boil, blanche three to four strips of bacon cut into one half inch pieces in boiling water in a small pan. Drain the bacon to get rid of most of the fat while retaining the wonderful bacon flavor, and add to the chicken broth. Add several sprigs of **thyme** (I like ten to twelve at least). Simmer a few minutes and add two cubed **potatoes** (skins on if you like, but scrub then well first). Make a roux of one cube of **margarine** (one quarter pound) with one-half cup of **flour**, until slightly brownish. Stir roux slowly into the soup mixture. Add two cups of **milk** (you can use reconstituted powdered milk for less fat and calories or part milk and part half-and-half — more calories, but great!). Add juice only (reserving the clams) from three six or seven-ounce cans of chopped or minced clams and four ripe **tomatoes,** Roma type if you can get them. Simmer for ten to fifteen minutes and then add the reserved clams. When serving, remove the thyme sprigs and for a final touch, add a few drops of **Spanish Sherry** that has been laced with **red pepper flakes.** This chowder can have the tomatoes omitted, or you may use fresh clams or other seafood.

Scallops with Thyme

Marinate one pound of **sea scallops** in equal parts of fresh **lemon juice** and **white wine** (I like sauterne) for twenty to thirty minutes. Warm a teaspoon of fresh thyme leaves (French or Lemon or Golden) in one tablespoon of **olive oil.** Heat oil to medium high in sauté pan and add drained scallops. Sauté until tender four to five minutes, but be careful not to overcook them. Serve immediately. If you wish you can cook the marinade down with any remaining oil in the pan for a drizzle over the fish.

Blend for Lamb

Mix together two teaspoons *each* of dried **thyme, rosemary, and parsley.** This can be used as a dry marinade before roasting, or mixed with herbal vinegar or wine as a wet marinade or baste.

Thyme Marinade

This marinade is especially good with fish. Combine two tablespoons of **olive oil,** one teaspoon dried **thyme** (or one tablespoon if using fresh), one-quarter teaspoon of fresh ground **black pepper**, a few drops of fresh **lemon juice** or an **herb vinegar**. Rub marinade on both sides of fish steak (try tuna or swordfish!). Marinate for fifteen or twenty minutes and then bake at 350° F. until done, 10-20 minutes depending on size and thickness of fish. The fish should flake easily when done but still moist in the center.

A Thymely Beer Bread

Stir together in a mixer bowl three and one-half cups of all purpose **flour** and two envelopes of dry active **yeast** (the fast-acting variety is best). In a saucepan, combine two cups water, two cups of **beer**, six tablespoons **brown sugar**, three tablespoons **oil**, and two teaspoons **salt**. Heat to warm (about 125° F.) and stir until the sugar dissolves. Beat this liquid mixture into the flour and yeast mixture with a mixer until well blended. Beat another six minutes and then add one slightly beaten **egg**. Beat one minute more. Stir in additional one cup of **white flour** and three cups of **whole wheat flour** along with four or more teaspoons of fresh **thyme** or a mixture of thyme, sage and rosemary. Let dough rise in a warmed bowl, covered. Stir it down and divide into three loaves and place in greased 5" by 9" loaf pans. Let rise again and bake at 375° F. for 25-35 minutes. Loaves should sound somewhat hollow when thumped when done. The tops should be browned. Wait ten minutes and remove from pans. Brush tops with melted butter. Cool before slicing. Makes 3 loaves.

Herbal Thyme Soap

Add two ounces of shredded **thyme** leaves to two cups of boiling **water**. Cover the pot and remove from the heat to steep for about 30 minutes. Strain the liquid and discard the leaves. You should have about twelve ounces of liquid remaining. Combine this herbal liquid with three ounces of a commercial floating **bath soap** cut into very small pieces. Melt the mixture over boiling water until it's smooth and blended. Pour into a container with a wide mouth and let stand, uncovered until cool. You may also pour into individual small containers such as frozen orange juice containers or small plastic milk cartons. Once cool, remove from the container and cut into individual bars. Lemon Thyme and Orange Balsam Thyme are good choices for this easy to make soap.

 Other Notes

Caraway Thyme and other creeping thymes can be used as a lawn because they are both durable and fragrant. This is about the toughest herb for a lawn and will create a thick, dark green mat within one year if planted in full sun in moderately rich, well drained soil. Water regularly until the plants become established.

Planting thyme near potatoes, tomatoes and eggplant is said to repel cabbage worms and whiteflies. Thyme attracts beneficial insects because it supplies shelter, nectar and pollen. Spiders, ground beetles, lacewings, lady beetles (or lady bugs), parasitic flies and predatory wasps are all attracted to fresh thyme.

Dried thyme leaves, however, are used to fumigate or repel insects because its odor is so strong. Egyptians used thyme in their embalming ointments. It is a powerful antiseptic and preservative.

The thymus gland in the chest received its name because it resembles the thyme flower.

Thymol oil is used in making colognes, aftershave lotions, soaps, and detergents.

And now it's thyme to leave this chapter behind us and proceed into the garden...

Epilogue

Why do I grow herbs?
Herbs make me happy when...

- The flavor of a meal is enhanced with herbs from my garden.

- My room is filled with the scents of old-fashioned roses, lavender, mint, and verbena potpourri.

- I chew a couple of fennel seeds and my hiccups stop.

- I sit in the garden and watch the butterflies and hummingbirds attracted by the Sweet Cicely.

- I enter my home and am greeted at the door with a beautiful herbal wreath of sage and bay that I created from my garden supplies.

- I ingest a feverfew leaf and my migraine headache is under control.

- I introduce someone new to the pleasures of herbs.

- I rinse my hair with sage or rosemary and it shines...I'm a brunette.

- My neighborhood children join me in the garden and I tell them legends and lore of fairies surrounding the thyme plants.

- I sit by a cozy fire scented with herbal rosemary stems, sipping a cup of peppermint tea on a cold winter's eve.

- My husband of thirty-one years gives me a rosemary oil back massage after too many hours at the computer.

- Most of all, herbs make me happy because they are never boring. They always leave me wanting to grow, use, learn about, touch, and smell more of these magnificent and useful plants. There are so many I have not yet grown in my gardens. I wonder if I will ever be able to know them all intimately?

Glossary of Terms

Analgesic: This is a substance that relieves pain by acting as a nervine or antispasmodic.

Annual: This type of plant completes its life cycle in one growing season; going from seed to flower and back to seed; examples are basil and summer savory.

Antibiotic: This is a substance produced by a microorganism that is capable of killing or inhibiting the growth of bacteria or other microorganisms.

Antioxidant: This is a chemical compound or substance that inhibits oxidation.

Antiseptic: This is a substance that destroys bacteria; usually applied to the skin to prevent infection.

Antispasmodic: This is a medicine that relieves or prevents involuntary muscle spasms or cramps such as those occurring in epilepsy, painful menstruation, intestinal cramping, or 'charley horses.'

Astringent: This is a substance that causes dehydration, tightening or shrinking of tissues and is used to stop bleeding, close skin pores, and tighten muscles.

Axil: This is the angle between the upper surface of a leafstalk, flower stalk, branch or similar part and the stem or axis from which it arises.

Biennial: This type of plant completes its life cycle in two physiological growing seasons (usually 2 years); examples are parsley and fennel. The seeds are produced on flower stalks in the second growing season.

Binomial Nomenclature: This is the botanical classification system which is the scientific way of naming plants using a two-name system; genus and species. Plant names are controlled by the International Congress of Botanical Nomenclature. The full botanical system includes units of **Kingdom, Division, Subdivison, Class, Subclass, Order, Family, Genus, Species, Botanical Variety, Cultivar**. Every binomial has meaning and is significant. See also: Genus & Species.

Botulism: This is an extremely dangerous food poisoning that can cause nerve damage and even death.

Bouquet Garni: This is a collection of various herbs (usually thyme, bay, and marjoram) tied up with string or in cheesecloth and used in cooking, stews, poultry, and fish dishes.

Bracts: This leaf-like plant part is located either below a flower or on the stalk of a flower cluster.

Bruising: This is a method of releasing the volatile oil within a seed, leaf or stem when using in culinary, medicinal or cosmetic form. This bruising can be done by slightly mashing in a mortar and pestle, or the leaves can be crushed gently in the hand.

B.t.: Bacillus thuringiensis is a bacterial insecticide which will work nicely if applied when caterpillars are young. B.t. is a stomach poison, not a contact poison.

Carminative: This is a substance that checks the formation of gas and helps dispel whatever gas has already formed in the intestinal tract.

Cloche: This is a bell-like glass or plastic vessel used to cover plants during cold spells or declining night temperatures to retain the daytime warmth.

Clone: This is an individual plant which is started by asexual propagation to create an identical plant.

Compress: This is made by folding cloth and moistening with an herbal infusion which is then applied to the skin. It is usually applied cold.

Corolla: This is the inner envelope of a flower, consisting of fused or separate petals.

Cough Syrups: See medicinal syrups.

Crystallizing Flower Blossoms: This is a process of preserving flower petals by using an egg white and fine sugar mixture.

Cultivar, cv.: This is a short version of 'cultivated variety'; a botanical term used to explain a variation within a species which is only maintained in cultivation. These cultivars are singled out because of their particular fragrance, color or form. Naming a variety of cultivar means adding a third or fourth word to the Latin genus and species: Thymus serphyllum 'Lemon Curd.'

Damping Off: This soil-borne fungal disease attacks seedlings at the soil line and kills them. Use a sterile soilless medium to prevent this from occurring.

Decoction: This is made by extracting an herbal essence which is obtained by boiling roots, bark or other substances. Boil these parts for 2-3 minutes & simmer 10 minutes. Decoctions may be applied externally or taken internally as a strong tea.

Espalier: This is the art of growing a plant in one plane; against a wall, trellis, or other flat support. These plants can also be trained against a house wall, a balcony fence, a screen on a terrace, a garden wall or in a freestanding container.

Dehydration: This form of preserving herbs may be done by using the sun (solar), a commercial dehydrator, a conventional oven, microwave oven, or by hanging the herbs in bunches.

Essential Oils: These are the concentrated vital essences of aromatic plants. They are a great boon to present-day potpourri blends for adding intensity and depth to a fragrant mixture, or in perfumery. Oils are particularly good for reviving a potpourri that has lost its scent. These oils must be used with discretion to avoid dominating subtler scents. Also used in aromatherapy, this volatile material derived from a plant usually bears the aroma or flavor of that plant. Oils won't mix with water but they are soluble in many organic solvents. Being volatile, they evaporate rapidly at room temperature.

Expectorant: This is a substance that, taken internally, helps the body expel phlegm through coughing, sneezing, or spitting.

Flatulence: This is a gas in the stomach or bowels. See also, Carminative.

Genus: This category in binominal nomenclature ranks below Family and above Species. It is used to describe a similar group of plants. Each genus in the plant kingdom has a unique name. It's common practice to talk about plants by their genus, or generic name; i.e. Mentha (mint genus), or Thymus (thyme genus).

Halitosis: This condition is characterized by stale or foul-smelling breath.

Herbaceous: This term describes a plant with a non-woody top. Green and leaf-like in appearance and texture, these plants will die down to ground level during the cold dormant season.

Herbfarm, The: A local business that specializes in herb plant sales, a catalogue business, workshops and classes, and a four-star restaurant. Address: 32804 SE Issaquah-Fall City Road, Fall City, Washington 98024.

Hybrid: This is a plant that is a cross between two species; usually forced, of mixed origin or composition.

Infusion: To make a medicinal infusion, pour boiled water over an herb in order to extract its active qualities.

Knot Garden: This is a design made with low compact herbs in an over-and-under lapping pattern within a defined space to create a symmetrical pattern. Good herb varieties include Dwarf Lavender, germander, low-growing artemisias, Lemon Thyme, hyssop, Dwarf Sage and santolina.

Living Foods Dehydrator: This company makes the wooden dehydrator that I have used for 25 years. I recommend it to all my students in food preservation classes. Address: PO Box 546, Fall City, Washington, 98024

Nosegay: See Tussie Mussie.

Ointment: Herbal ointment bases are made from pure lard, white petroleum jelly, or bees wax and olive oil. Ointments can be stored for lengthy periods of time.

Perennial: These plants grow three or more seasons in their appropriate climate.

pH: Pronounced pee-aach; p(otential) of H(ydrogen) is a noun in chemistry that measures the acidity or alkalinity of a solution (soil). Measurements are from 1 to 14; 7 is neutral: the higher alkaline the higher the number 7.5, 8.0, etc.; the lower the number the more acidity 6.8, 5.7, 4.5 etc.

Poultice: This is a soft composition of crushed herbs placed in a muslin cloth, heated and applied directly to the affected part, soothing and drawing out the irritants.

Potpourri: This is from the French word for pot, and 'pourrir' (to rot). A mixture of sweet-scented herbs — Orange Mint, thyme, rosemary, Rose Geranium, Lemon Verbena, Lemon Balm, Sweet Marjoram, Sweet Basil, tarragon — can provide dried leaves for making potpourri. Ingredients, including spices, are usually kept in a whole or semi-whole state.

Rose Water: This is made by simmering handfuls of fresh rose petals in water for 30 minutes; straining and refrigerating.

Sachet: This can be made for the bath by tieing handfuls of dried leaves or petals in squares of cheesecloth; rosemary, thyme, comfrey, basil, mint and lavender are good choices. Sachet ingredients are generally crumbled or ground as opposed to potpourri which is left in a whole state.

Scarifying: This is a method of preparing seeds for swifter sprouting. Because some hard seed coats prevent them from taking up the moisture necessary for germination, pre-treating such seeds — either by soaking them in water or scarifying the seed coats — is often the difference between success and failure. The method of scarifying seed is to nick the seed coat to speed water uptake without damaging the embryo. You can either use a file or a knife, or rub seeds between two pieces of sandpaper.

Species: A species is a kind of plant comprising all the individuals that share common attributes and are capable of interbreeding freely with one another but not with members of another species. Any number from one to hundreds of species that are similar in meaningful ways can be combined into a genus.

Sterile Soil: This is a mixture that contains little or no nutrients; minerals, phosphorous, nitrogen, etc., usually used to establish cuttings.

Stimulant: This is a substance that increases or quickens the various functional actions of the body, such as hastening digestion, raising body temperature or heart rate, and so on. The substance does this quickly, unlike a tonic, which stimulates general health over a period of time.

Stolons: These are underground runners that produce new stems at a distance from the parent plant.

Stratification: This is a cold period needed for germination of seeds that is normally required and supplied in winter time. If you collect seed in late summer or early fall, you have to fulfill the requirement by cold stratification in the refrigerator. Collect sharp sand, wet it, and let the excess water run off. Put a teaspoon of moist sand in a 35mm film canister with the seed, label and date it, and set it in the refrigerator. Stratification usually requires 3-6 weeks, depending on the species. Longer exposure won't matter too much but too short a time may not satisfy the cold-period requirement.

Strewing Herbs: During the Middle Ages, herbs were often strewn on the floor, to repel fleas, lice, moths and insect pests. They also masked unsavory smells and provided insulation against the cold in winter and the heat in summer. This practice is unsuitable today, but sprigs of herbs can be placed under doormats or carpets, or perhaps on the porch. Choose from the following: balm, basil, chamomile, thyme, lavender and rosemary. Particularly fragrant herbs such as lavender, mint and rosemary were used to scatter on bare floors for the purpose of covering unwanted odors caused by animals or guests who did not bathe.

Syrups, Medicinal: These are made by adding crushed herbs to boiling water. The water is then cooled, strained and rewarmed with sugar and boiled until syrupy.

Tincture: These are made by extracting oils of roots or leaves of herbs by placing in alcohol instead of water. After a period of darkness, the strained liquid is used in concentrated form.

Tisane: This is an old-fashioned name for tea that is made from an infusion and generally drunk for medicinal purposes.

Tonic Herbs: These herbs give tone and vigor to the body's systems, providing a general feeling of well-being. Substances that invigorate or strengthen the system, these tonics often act as stimulants.

Tussie Mussie: This is a tight little bouquet of aromatic leaves and flowers that is placed in a sometimes elaborate holder. (A round doily with a hole in the middle for the stems works well.) These are also called nosegays.

Umbel: This is a flat-top or rounded flower cluster in which the individual flower stalks arise from about the same point as in the carrot, parsley and related plants.

Variety, var.: This is a fairly consistent, naturally occurring variation within a species of plants.

Volatile Oil: This is the aromatic essence of the herb contained in its leaves and stems that is easily dissipated when the leaves are pre-crumbled or subjected to heat.

Whorls: These are floral clusters in which each individual flower is attached by its own stem to a common point at the top of the stalk. An example is lavender.

Zest: This is the colored portion of the skin of a citrus fruit; i.e. lemon, orange, lime. This does not include the pith, or white portion under the zest. The pith is very bitter and should not be used. To obtain only the zest of a fruit use a potato peeler.

Index

About the Author

Carol Peterson's work and study of herbs spans more than 20 years. The popular Pacific Northwest herb specialist regularly leads seminars, teaches classes, and contributes articles on herbs and gardening. Carol's expertise includes herb gardening for the home, cooking and culinary uses of herbs, and applying herbs medicinally, cosmetically and decoratively — all with practical, easy-to- master techniques.

In addition to having trained alongside other renowned herb experts, Carol holds King County Master Gardener and Food Advisor certifications and is an active member of the International Herb Growers and Marketers Association (IHGMA), Herb Society of America and several gardening organizations.

Carol is the owner of the company, **Fresh From the Garden**, and resides in Snoqualmie, Washington with her husband, Charles, and her 80 species herb garden.

Order Form

Postal Orders: Mountain Garden Publishing, Inc.
                       PO Box 98-A
                       Snoqualmie, WA 98065

Telephone Order: (206) 888-0773
                       Have your VISA or MasterCard ready.

Please send _____ copy(s)of the following book. I understand
that I may return any books for a full refund — for any reason,
no questions asked.

          "Herbs You Can Master"
          A Primer For Herbal Enthusiasts

No. of Copies @ $13.95 each: _____

Sales Tax: Please add 8.2% for books shipped to
                    Washington State address.

Shipping: Book Rate: $2.00 for the first book and 75¢
                    for each additional book. (Surface
                    shipping may take three to four weeks.)
                    Air Mail: $3.50 per book

Total $ _____

Payments:

_____ Check Enclosed

_____ Credit card: [   ] **VISA** [   ] MasterCard

Card number: _____

Name on card: _____ Exp. date: ___

Signature: _____